Printed in the United States of America First Printing, 2020
ISBN 978-0-9978499-6-7
Phantom Plastics LLC
2 Denison Lane
Terrace Park, OH 45174 USA

Disclaimer
This publication contains the ideas and opinions of its author. It is intended to provide helpful and informative material on the topics addressed in the publication. It is based on the author's knowledge and recollection of events, related to the best of his knowledge. Incidents are related to highlight issues and are not intended to portray any given company or individual in a negative light. The author does not assume and hereby disclaims any liability to any party for any loss, damage, or disruption caused by errors or omissions, whether such errors or omissions result from accident, negligence, or any other cause. If you do not agree to be bound by this disclaimer, please discontinue reading.

Contents

PREFACE

I once sat next to a young person on a plane. She took a nap and I glanced at a sticker on her laptop that read: "Rise above plastics". I had to smile at the naivety. Why? Well, the sticker was made of plastic, and so was the adhesive that held it on her laptop, which was also made of plastic. Her backpack was made of nylon plastic, and so were her shoes. She had a PET plastic water bottle in her hand and was cozied up in a polyester (plastic) blanket. In fact, the only thing I could see that wasn't synthetic plastic was her cotton jacket. Later, she woke up and started editing video clips made on her ABS plastic GoPro camera—in the video, she was swimming in the ocean in a rubber suit with plastic flippers on. She had no idea that her life would not be possible without the very plastics she claimed to object to.

That incident made me think—there must be many people who are against plastic but who don't fully understand what it would mean to live without it. I have spent my whole career as a plastic materials scientist, so to me it's obvious, but how are the public supposed to know? In fact, how can the public be sure of anything these days when extreme headlines go viral and misinformation spreads at the speed of light? You would think that eventually the truth would come out and public opinion would correct itself, but scientists have studied that, and it turns out that the sensational lies spread faster and farther than the truth. So, when the truth does finally come out, it never catches up with the lie. Why is that? Well, the truth is often not as exciting as the lie was.

Over the last decade or so, there has been a vocal campaign against plastics and the plastics industry has done almost nothing to counter it. Perhaps they assumed it would go away. However, it didn't go away, so now we are ten years on and the public has made up their minds that plastics are bad. Politicians make policies in response to that public opinion, and companies make policies and even create new product lines to address the public's demands. Progress is being made in the war on plastics, and that must be a good thing, right?

I didn't think too much about it until recently when my two daughters came home from school and told me what they had learned that day. To my horror, they had been taught clear, undeniable lies about plastic. I should not have been so surprised—after all, teachers are just members of the public, and they pick up their information from the same online sources we are all exposed to. However, it's a serious problem when we start teaching our children lies. They will grow up and vote for policies based on those lies, and that is likely to have unforeseen—and unfortunate—consequences.

So, what was the lie that triggered me? My kids were told that plastics take a thousand years to degrade. As someone who has spent my whole career as a plastic materials scientist, I know that's a whopping lie. I had a BSc, a master's, a PhD and 30 years of experience telling me this was just plain wrong. The fact that plastics degrade is as certain as the sun rising or an apple falling. It's not open for debate. There are thousands of scientific articles on it, and a whole journal called Polymer Degradation and Stability devoted to the topic.

Just how stable are the typical plastics we use today? I had just finished a project as an expert witness for a large class-action lawsuit, which led to appearances on CBS's 60 Minutes, Sky News, and the BBC. It was all about the stability of polypropylene mesh used in the body to repair hernias and other abdominal ailments. I had just read hundreds of peer-reviewed articles on the stability of polypropylene and other plastics, so I had the information at my fingertips. Would you like to guess how long polypropylene lasts at room temperature? Please take a guess…

The answer is that polypropylene (PP) is extremely unstable. Scientists found that out almost as soon as they made PP for the first time. If left at room temperature, it will oxidize and degrade, losing its strength in less than one year.

Does that shock you? That's what the peer-reviewed scientific articles tell us. It's a fact proven in the laboratory. That's a big deal, because polypropylene is the second-most common plastic produced today. You use it every day in household items like shampoo bottle caps (especially the ones with the hinge), pot scrubbers, and string. It's the main plastic used in cars due to its attractive properties and low weight. It's not just PP, either. Other common plastics degrade rather rapidly too. My kids had been told a blatant lie.

How can it be that this accepted "fact" that plastics take hundreds or thousands of years to degrade has penetrated our minds, our schools, and our policies? It turns out that a lie begins to sounds like the truth if it is repeated enough. Of course, it's still a lie, but everyone will believe it. This is exactly what the plastics industry has allowed to happen. It made me wonder about the other "facts" we all believe about plastic. If this one was a lie, what about the others? The first thing I did was to check whether plastic bags really are bad for the environment. Can you guess what I found? I found several studies from all around the world and every single one of them showed that plastic bags are far greener than either paper or cotton. Shocking, isn't it?

Now, I was even more suspicious. I started downloading articles on plastic waste, litter, microplastics, and other related topics. I spent a year reading several hundred articles so that I could present them to the teachers at my kid's school. Members of the public often make up their mind and then only read articles that confirm what they already believe, but that's not how a professional scientist works. I had to read every article I could find and only then make up my mind, based on the evidence. It was a preposterous amount of work, but that was the only way to get to the bottom of the matter.

You are about to see the evidence from scientists all around the world, as published in peer-reviewed journals. I will cite their work and quote from the studies word-for-word to avoid any "spin". In this book, you will discover that everything you have been told about plastics and the environment is a lie, and you will be left with a choice. Hopefully, you will take the real facts and start fighting for a brighter future. Or, you can continue believing the lies you have been told online, which means you will be fighting for changes that seriously harm, rather than help, our environment. It's that simple.

"When you see a text box, like this one, you are reading a verbatim quote, usually taken from the abstract or conclusions section of a peer-reviewed scientific study."

When you see some small text like this, it is the citation to the study, so you can go look it up yourself. This is how professionals show that what they have said is backed by evidence.

As a guide to reading the book, when you see a box like the one below, it is a headline from a newspaper or other print article.

As I mentioned, this book is based on over 400 scientific articles and reports. It would be cumbersome to list every single one here, so I have provided a comprehensive list at plasticsparadox.com. That way the list can grow as new articles are published.

We are told that plastics are our saviour and our nemesis. That is the "Plastics Paradox". How can they be our friend and our enemy at the same time? How do we know whether to promote or persecute plastics? To discover the answer, we need to present the evidence to you, the jury, the public. Only then can we make an informed decision.

INTRODUCTION

THE PLASTICS PARADOX

FACTS FOR A BRIGHTER FUTURE

INTRODUCTION

When making important decisions, responsible people take extra care to do their research. The more important the decision, the more effort we invest. When buying a car, most of us spend time reading online reviews and the opinions of professionals with years of experience. You, the reader, deserve respect for checking to see what's really going on with plastic. It is an important topic, and understanding the facts is the only way to make wise choices for future generations.

Now, let's consider the uproar about plastics and the environment. We can all agree that it's an important topic, but what do we really know about it? I have seen countless articles online, and most have one thing in common: they are not by experts and they contain no proven facts. What do I mean by that? Professional articles list sources and refer back to peer-reviewed science. If an article doesn't do that, then it's worthless.

It's shocking to me that public opinions about plastic are based on articles with neither data nor substance. Our children and our planet's future deserve better than that.

> "Without data you're just a person with an opinion."
> W. Edwards Deming

Here's one example to illustrate the point. A story claimed that Americans use 500 million single-use plastic straws per day. That number was repeated by the New York Times, Washington Post, National Geographic, CNN, Fox News, Wall Street Journal, USA Today, environmental groups, and countless other publications. None of them checked the figure or where it had come from. Where did it come from? It was later revealed that the source was Milo Cress, a 9-year-old schoolboy. He had no proof for the data, and when the number was eventually checked, it was found to be wrong. The actual number was far lower.

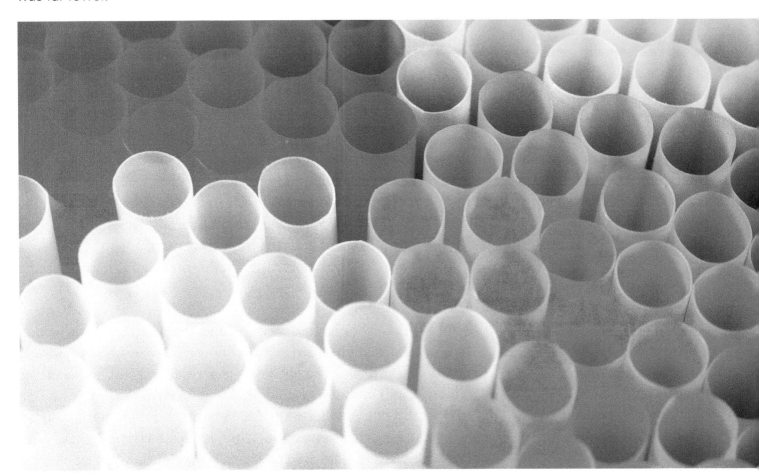

How a 9-Year-Old Boy's Statistic Shaped a Debate on Straws, New York Times
Niraj Chokshi, July 19th 2018

This is exactly how lies about the environment spread. The more sensational the claim, the more readily it is repeated. When the truth is finally learned, that news does not travel as fast or as wide, so the truth never catches up with the lie.

This book is about exposing the truth so that smart, caring people can act on it. In the case of single-use straws, Marriott, Starbucks, McDonalds and more have banned straws based on a lie. They replaced them with paper straws that cost more, don't work as well, and as you will discover later, are actually far worse for the environment. This example shows why we need facts before we act.

As a professional scientist, it worries me that everyone has made up their mind on this topic in a vacuum of information. Think back to when you formed your opinions. Did you see a YouTube video? Maybe it was a LinkedIn article, or even a newspaper article. That is rumour, not science, and it does not provide a basis upon which to form a sound opinion.

As a leading plastic materials scientist, I could instantly spot that some of what we were being told was totally untrue—and that was enough to make me investigate further. I decided to look for the science and see what I could uncover. A good scientist reads everything they can find before making up their mind, so I went on a mission and reviewed over 400 articles. I was continually waiting for the moment when I would find an article that proved plastics were our enemy. I read and I read, article after article, and that moment never came. What I found was exactly the opposite. In this book, I share what I found with you.

I should probably explain why you should trust what I'm writing. One reason is that I am one of the world's top plastic materials scientists. In terms of qualifications, I am a PhD chemist, Chartered Chemist, and a Fellow of the Royal Society of Chemistry. Companies like HP, P&G, iRobot, Disney, CBS, Sky News, the BBC and many more trust me and turn to me for help. I would not be able to make a living without high integrity because the Fortune 100 would not trust me with their secrets. I do not sell or market plastic—rather, my career has been as a professional scientist. So, when I make a claim, I always back it up with data and links to the peer-reviewed science so you can check it for yourself. You don't even have to believe me because everything can be checked.

As well as listing my sources, I have quoted many of the studies word for word so that there can be no accusation of "spin". After reading this book, you will be one of a handful who knows the truth and can see a clear path to the preservation of our environment. A path that actually works.

In writing this book, I know that I am going against what is politically correct at the moment. The book will not make me popular. However, the facts speak for themselves and we cannot make progress based on the foundation of lies that we have now. Therefore, I feel compelled to proceed regardless. Ideally, the plastics industry would have spoken up in the last decade, as these lies were being repeated over and over. Unfortunately, they chose not to, and now public opinion has already turned against plastics. As you will soon discover, that opinion is completely unfounded.

WHAT ARE PLASTICS ANYWAY?

Commonly occurring molecules we talk about every day include water, acetone, alcohol, and so on. These are all small molecules. Plastics, however, are a type of very large molecule called polymers, where "poly" means many and "mer" means unit. People tend to be wary of anything unfamiliar, but it turns out that some of our favourite things in nature are made of polymers. One example is collagen, which keeps your skin healthy. Another is cellulose, which is what holds trees and plants together. Silk is made of polymers, and so are cotton and wool. We eat polymers all the time. For example, Casein, a protein in the milk we drink. Our very existence depends on polymers. The enzymes that make our bodies function are polymeric molecules, and even DNA, the blueprint for all life on Earth, is a polymer.

Some decades ago, scientists discovered how to make their own polymers which we often refer to as plastics. Plastics have ushered in a technological revolution leading to stunning advances in our quality of life. Plastic pipes deliver clean drinking water and plastic-insulated wires deliver electricity. The rapid adoption and sudden prevalence of plastics have created a backlash, and we will look to see whether that is truly justified or more of a knee-jerk reaction.

PLASTICS - SHORT FOR THERMOPLASTICS

Thermoplastics are polymers that can be melted and formed into sheets or complex parts. Thermoplastics like polyethylene (PE), polypropylene (PP), polyvinyl chloride (PVC), polystyrene (PS), and nylon (PA6 and PA6,6) get their strength from polymer chain entanglements. If the chains are too short, then molecular entanglements cannot form, so the material has no strength. Imagine very short spaghetti strands. Short spaghetti strands do not hold together, whereas when you try to lift up long strands of cooked spaghetti, the whole bunch comes up in a tangled lump. It's the same with plastic polymers. The long chains get tangled together. We will hear more about chain entanglements later.

On the other hand, thermosetting polymers have a different structure. Instead of entanglements, the molecules are all joined together in one continuous network instead of entangled straight chains. The 3D network is strongly bonded and is effectively one giant molecule, so unlike thermoplastics, thermosets do not flow when heated. A common example of a thermoset is epoxy resin. This type of polymer is not called "plastic" because it does not flow when heated.

WHAT DO POLYMER MOLECULES LOOK LIKE?

A polyethylene chain made from 10,000 monomer units joined together would be about two Ångströms across and 25,000Å long (2.5µm). An Ångström is one ten-billionth of a meter, which is too small to imagine, so let's go back to our spaghetti analogy. If the polymer chain were as thick as a piece of spaghetti, how long would the spaghetti strand have to be in order to have the same proportions as a polymer chain? The answer is about 25 meters (about 25 yards) long. So, visualize a piece of spaghetti as long as two school buses and you have the right relative dimensions.

A polymer chain as wide as a spaghetti strand would be two busses long

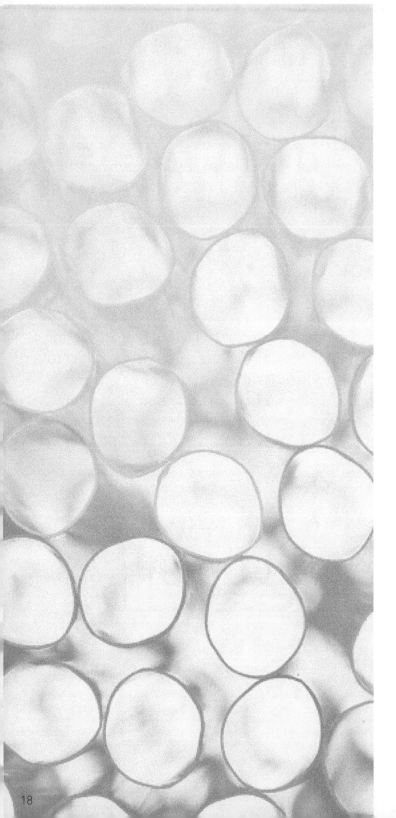

It's easy to understand why polymer chains get tangled up so easily. If the polymer chain were a strand of human hair, then the hair would be about three feet long. I think anyone who has had hair that long knows how easily it gets tangled. Polymer chains can be even longer—take for example the ultra-high molecular weight polyethylene (UHMWPE), which is sold under the trade name Dyneema® and is used to make bulletproof vests and cut-resistant gloves. If a UHMWPE chain had the same thickness as a piece of spaghetti, it would be over 20 busses long. In the hair analogy, the UHMWPE chains would be over 30 feet long! Such long polymer chains entangle even more and give exceptional strength—in this case, strong enough to stop a bullet.

HOW SAFE ARE POLYMERS?

As we have seen, polymers are very long and large molecules. What does that mean when it comes to safety? Well, for one thing, polymers don't have any smell. It is fundamentally impossible for them to smell because there's no way for polymer chains to evaporate and reach your nose. They have no taste, and by the same token, they cannot pass through your skin. In fact, polymers are considered so safe that the FDA created a polymer rule whereby polymers are considered safe for the reasons given above. It is known as the FDA polymer exemption.

PLASTICS IN OUR LIVES

It would be unfair and unbalanced to write a book only on the negative perception of plastics without mentioning the good that plastics do.

Plastics such as polyester and nylon are used to make our clothes. Toys, containers, and innumerable other items are made from various types of plastic. Kevlar® and Dyneema® vests stop bullets and save lives, as do the Nomex® outfits that the fire department rely on to protect them from flames. Medical devices rely heavily on plastic. In many instances, it is the only material that works. The list of uses is almost infinite, but there are a couple more items that cannot be overlooked. Plastic pipes bring us clean water, and plastic-insulated wires bring us electricity. Without plastic, we would have no electricity, no cell phones, no laptops or computers of any kind, and no internet to use them on. Many people are not aware of the many uses of plastics and what a plastic-free world would really mean. When considering any topic, we need to carefully weigh the pros and the cons before deciding on the best course of action.

CONCLUSIONS

So, now we have an idea what polymers and plastics are. We know they occur in nature and are just very long molecules, which are considered safe.

Here's what we now believe about plastics:

1. Plastics are bad for the environment, so we must replace them
2. Plastics leads to a waste problem, so we must use less plastic
3. Plastics take 1,000 years to degrade, so we must move to degradable options
4. Plastics cause litter, so we must replace them with paper and degradable materials
5. Microplastics in the ocean are harming marine life, so we must ban disposable plastic items

Plastics have been tried in the court of public opinion and found guilty. Unfortunately, the trial was conducted without any evidence. That's right, plastics have been convicted based purely on gossip. No one bothered to check what the science says about all of this. Why is that? Part of the reason is that it's much more work to check the facts. It takes hundreds of hours of painstaking research. Until now, no one has been prepared to face that daunting task and present the findings for all to see.

You are about to discover that the peer-reviewed science disproves every one of the statements above. This has huge consequences. It means we need to change course if we want to preserve our planet for future generations. If you want to help the environment, I applaud you—and when you have finished this book, you will be a powerful force for good.

CHAPTER ONE
THE MEANING OF GREEN

THE MEANING OF GREEN

These days, everyone wants to be green, or at least look like they are paying attention to the environment. This has led to big businesses creating new products to vie for your dollars. It has become so prevalent that some companies are accused of "greenwashing," whereby they fake being green in order to create a good impression and make a sale. How can a citizen or a corporation be sure what is truly green and what is not? I first learned the answer to that at a party in Stockholm in the mid-1990s.

WHAT IS AN LCA?

Sweden is a leader in environmental responsibility, and even back then they were diligently collecting glass bottles and other items for recycling. It made everyone feel good because they were helping the community. I was chatting with a friend of mine who worked at a large pharmaceutical company. He told me about something called a lifecycle analysis (LCA) as a tool to see what was really "green". He explained that a lifecycle analysis is where you look at everything needed to make a product, including raw materials, energy, waste, by-products, transportation, waste, disposal, and so on. You have to add it all up and see what the total environmental burden of the item is. I told him it sounded fascinating but also like a lot of work. He said it was a lot of work, but it was the only way to be sure of an accurate answer. He told me about an LCA on glass bottles. In Sweden, they collect all the bottles and drive them to Norway where the processing plant melts them to make new bottles. The result of the LCA was that it was not green to collect and recycle glass bottles in Sweden. All the CO_2 created by the trucking meant it was greener to go to the beach, get some sand, and make new bottles from that.

L. L. Gaines and M. M. Mintz, Energy Implications of Glass-Container Recycling, ANL/ESD-18, NREL/TP-430-5703, UC Category: 249, DE94000288 1994

That is when I learned that the obvious answer is not necessarily the right answer when it comes to determining what's green. Going by gut instinct doesn't work. The whole of Sweden was feeling great that they deposited and recycled their bottles, but that well-intentioned action was actually harming the environment instead of helping it. I asked my friend why that was happening, and he said it was probably the government trying to raise awareness about the environment. I thought it was strange to raise awareness by forcing people to do something proven harmful to the environment. Perhaps, because LCA was new back then, the government were unaware that they were doing more harm than good.

Molten glass is processed at ~1100°C (~2200°F), which is very energy intensive

HOW IS LIFECYCLE ANALYSIS OR LCA DEFINED?

"Life-cycle assessment (LCA, also known as life-cycle analysis, ecobalance, and cradle-to-grave analysis) is a technique to assess environmental impacts associated with all the stages of a product's life from raw material extraction through materials processing, manufacture, distribution, use, repair and maintenance, and disposal or recycling."

Source: Wikipedia's "Life-cycle assessment" page

Thankfully, these days, LCA is a lot more common. You don't have to do it all from scratch because there are databases with most (or all) of the information—computer programs can also make it simpler. There is an ISO standard, so everyone uses the exact same approach, and the results are audited by external experts to make sure that there is no bias. Companies all around the world are using LCA, and environmental groups like Greenpeace use it too. In fact, it is the only accepted way to determine what really is green.

PLASTIC BAGS LCA

We have all heard the outcry about plastic bags. I have read countless articles, and not a single one had any evidence one way or the other about whether plastic bags were green compared to the other options like paper or cotton. As you can imagine, the first thing I did was to Google "LCA plastic bag". I was delighted, and a little surprised, to get hits right away. There were LCA studies available for free as pdf files for anyone to read. What did they say? Well, the first one said that the standard polyethylene bag was the greenest option if all bags are used only once. However, a reusable polypropylene bag was even greener after a few uses. So, plastic came in first and second place. What about paper? Paper bags, even ones from recycled paper, were far worse than plastic. They require more energy, more CO_2 emissions, more water, and more chemicals to make. How about cotton? I've seen plenty of posts online about people proudly taking their cotton totes in order to be green. The LCA showed that cotton was disastrous for the environment, and organic cotton was even worse. You would have to reuse a cotton bag over 100 times for it to break even with the single-use plastic bags we use today.

How do we know which one is actually green?

This came as a surprise to me, but as a scientist, I needed to see more than one study to be sure. So, I did more searches for terms like "LCA grocery bag," "lifecycle analysis plastic bag," and so on. In the end, I found every LCA study from all around the world by scientists in Denmark, US, UK, Canada, Australia, and more. They all agreed that the greenest bags are made from plastic. Let me restate that. There was no cherry-picking. Every single study ever done shows plastic bags are greenest. I even challenged a PhD chemist friend of mine to see if I'd missed any LCA studies. He searched and searched and finally agreed that I had found them all, and they all said plastics are the greenest alternative.

This was conclusive proof that what we have all been told is just plain wrong. Why demonize plastic bags when the evidence says that replacing them does more harm than good? The same lies have been repeated so often that most people accept them without question, but now you know better because you took the time to check the facts. When they ask you "paper or plastic" in the supermarket, you can hold your head high and say, "Plastic please, it's better for the environment". That's what I say. I just wish that the CEO of Kroger had read the studies, because they have announced they are about to ban plastic bags. As I said, if you start with faulty information, then you make decisions that harm the environment instead of helping it.

PLASTIC BAGS ARE GREENEST – PROOF, PROOF & MORE PROOF

For years, we have been told that plastic bags are bad. The vast majority of the general public have fallen for that narrative, and it is hard to change people's minds once they are already made up. Studies have shown that people will believe lies if they hear them enough, and even people with high IQ are not immune.

M. Warren, Higher Intelligence And An Analytical Thinking Style Offer No Protection Against "The Illusory Truth Effect" – Our Tendency To Believe Repeated Claims Are True, Research Digest, June 26th 2019

So how can we get people to change their mind? I am a realist, so I know that for some people, no amount of evidence will help. Their opinions are based on emotion and are set in stone. However, wiser, more open-minded people can be persuaded if the case is strong enough, and this book is for those people. Here are three reasons to discard the falsehoods and embrace the truth:

1. What we have been told is not credible because it comes from non-experts such as hack journalists with click-bait headlines vying for views
2. The assertion that "plastics are bad" has zero support from scientific studies; it is pure fiction (more on that later)
3. It is vital to align ourselves with the facts because that is the only way to make wise decisions that help, rather than harm, our environment

Having spent months looking for LCA studies on grocery bags, every study shows that plastic is the best choice. Bear in mind that these studies were performed in different countries by independent organizations spanning two decades. Let me show you the conclusions from each study. If you are already convinced, then feel free to skim through the rest of this section. Extraordinary proof is needed when fighting the prevailing view, so I will take up that challenge and present several LCA studies I have found.

STUDY 1 – CLEMSON UNIVERSITY

"A compilation of all of the statistically-based, scientific studies of litter in the U.S. and Canada over an 18 year period shows consistently that 'plastic bags' (which includes trash bags, grocery bags, retail bags and dry cleaning bags) make up a very small portion of litter, usually less than 1%."

"Our results also show that Paper bags, even with 100% recycle content, have significantly higher average impacts on the environment than either of the reusable bags or single-use plastic retail bags."

"Our results in this study show that these regulations and policies may result in negative impact on the environment rather than positive. Even though Paper bags come from a renewable resource and are easily recycled, it is likely that they are not the best environmental choice."

R. M. Kimmel, Life Cycle Assessment of Grocery Bags in Common Use in the United States, Environmental Studies, Clemson University Digital Press 2014

In summary, they found that paper bags are much worse for the environment and that the best two choices were reusable polypropylene bags or single-use polyethylene bags. They also note that plastic bags are not really a significant problem in the first place.

STUDY 2 – FRANKLIN ASSOCIATES

"The study results support the conclusion that any decision to ban traditional polyethylene plastic grocery bags in favor of bags made from alternative materials (compostable plastic or recycled paper) will be counterproductive and result in a significant increase in environmental impacts across a number of categories from global warming effects to the use of precious potable water resources."

"This study supports the conclusion that the standard polyethylene grocery bag has significantly lower environmental impacts than a 30% recycled paper bag and a compostable plastic bag."

Resource and Environmental Profile Analysis of Polyethylene and Unbleached Paper Grocery Sacks, Franklin Associates Ltd for the Council for Solid Waste Solutions 1990

Plastic bags were found to be even greener than recycled paper bags.

STUDY 3 – DANISH EPA

"In general, LDPE carrier bags, which are the bags that are always available for purchase in Danish supermarkets, are the carriers providing the overall lowest environmental impacts when not considering reuse. In particular, between the types of available carrier bags, LDPE carrier bags with rigid handle are the most preferable. Effects of littering for this type of bag were considered negligible for Denmark."

Life Cycle Assessment of grocery carrier bags, Environmental Project no. 1985, The Danish Environmental Protection Agency 2018

The study found that polyethylene bags were best. They also noted that litter was not an issue, presumably because Denmark handles their waste effectively.

STUDY 4 – UK

"The conventional HDPE bag had the lowest environmental impacts of the lightweight bags in eight of the nine impact categories."

"The paper bag has to be used four or more times to reduce its global warming potential to below that of the conventional HDPE bag, but was significantly worse than the conventional HDPE bag for human toxicity and terrestrial ecotoxicity due to the effect of paper production. However, it is unlikely the paper bag can be regularly reused the required number of times due to its low durability."

"The cotton bag has a greater impact than the conventional HDPE bag in seven of the nine impact categories even when used 173 times (i.e. the number of uses required to reduce the GWP of the cotton bag to that of the conventional HDPE bag with average secondary reuse). The impact was considerably larger in categories such as acidification and aquatic & terrestrial ecotoxicity due to the energy used to produce cotton yarn and the fertilisers used during the growth of the cotton."

C. Edwards & J. M. Fry, Life cycle assessment of supermarket carrier bags: a review of the bags available in 2006, Report: SC030148, Environment Agency 2011

Standard polyethylene bags were greener in almost every possible way. Paper was worse for the environment and reusable cotton bags were disastrous.

The next study is from the Reason Foundation. They are described as an American libertarian think-tank. Some may say that their study should be excluded for fear of possible political bias. I have no political views, and as their conclusions are the same as all the other studies, I see no evidence of bias and therefore no sound reason to exclude their conclusions. The message is the same, whether or not you choose to give more or less credence to any one of them.

STUDY 5 – REASON FOUNDATION

"Proponents claim that banning plastic shopping bags will benefit the environment. Yet, as this study has shown, there is very little empirical support for such claims. Indeed, the evidence seems to point in the other direction for most environmental effects. Some of the alleged benefits are simply false, such as the claim that eliminating plastic bags will reduce oil consumption."

"Unfortunately, policymakers have been cajoled into passing ordinances that ban plastic bags. That is bad news for consumers. It is also bad news for the environment, since the public has been misled into believing that by restricting the use of plastic bags, the problems for which those bags are allegedly responsible will be dramatically reduced."

J. Morris & B. Seasholes, How Green Is that Grocery Bag Ban? An Assessment of the Environmental and Economic Effects of Grocery Bag Bans and Taxes, Reason Foundation 2014

They found that plastic bags are the best option and that replacing them would not reduce oil consumption. They also point out that the public and policymakers have been misled into making decisions that actually harm the environment.

STUDY 6 – SOUTH AFRICA

"As a first order assessment, it can be reliably concluded that plastic bags have a smaller environmental footprint for use ratios of up to 2.5 plastic bags to one paper bag. Above this ratio, the uncertainty of data accuracy is too high to form reliable conclusions. Only for very high ratios of 7:1 and above does the paper bag begin to compete with the plastic bag."

J. Sevitz, A. C. Brent and A.B. Fourie, An environmental comparison of plastic and paper consumer bags in South Africa: Implications for the Local Manufacturing Industry, SA Journal of Industrial Engineering,14(1): 67-82 2003

Once again, plastic bags are found to be far greener than paper.

- "Reusable bags have lower environmental impacts than all of the bags with only 1–3 typical uses.
- A substantial shift to more durable bags would deliver environmental gains through reductions in greenhouse gases, energy and water use, resource depletion and litter.
- The reusable PET bag with 100% post-consumer recycled content was found to achieve the greatest environmental benefits, closely followed by the non-woven plastic (polypropylene) 'Green Bag'.
- The shift from one single use bag to another single use bag may improve one environmental outcome, but be offset by another environmental impact. As a result, no single-use bag produced an overall benefit.
- Recycled content in bags generally led to lowering the overall environmental impact of bags.
- From a climate change perspective the paper bags performed most poorly, due in large part to their relatively high weight."

LCA of shopping bag alternatives - Final Report, Hyder Consulting Pty Ltd
for Zero Waste South Australia 2009

Plastic bags were found to be greenest, with reusable PP and PET bags best of all. Paper bags performed badly due to their high weight (~10x more than PE).

WHAT TYPE OF PLASTIC BAG IS GREENEST?

So, after looking at all the studies, which type of plastic bag wins? The consensus is that the standard disposable PE bag is greenest and even better if it's reused at least once (as a trash can liner, for instance). The reusable PP bag wins if it's reused several times, but studies have highlighted some downsides to reusable bags. If reusable bags aren't sanitized properly after each use, they can harbour dangerous bacteria.

C. Gerba, Assessment of the Potential for Cross Contamination of Food Products by Reusable Shopping Bags, University of Arizona, June 9th 2010

Mould, yeast, and bacteria were found in reusable plastic bags. Conclusions of the study included:

"The test findings clearly support concerns that reusable grocery bags can become an active microbial habitat and a breeding ground for bacteria, yeast, mold, and coliforms."

"This study provides strong evidence that reusable bags could pose a significant risk to the safety of the food supply if used to transport food from store to home."

Grocery Carry Bag Sanitation - A Microbiological Study of Reusable Bags and 'First or single-use' Plastic Bags, Environment and Plastics Industry Council 2009

Another publication looked for any health effects recorded due to single-use plastic bag bans. Here is an excerpt from their conclusions:

"We examine deaths and emergency room admissions related to these bacteria in the wake of the San Francisco ban. We find that both deaths and ER visits spiked as soon as the ban went into effect. Relative to other counties, deaths in San Francisco increase by almost 50 percent, and ER visits increase by a comparable amount. Subsequent bans by other cities in California appear to be associated with similar effects. Conservative estimates of the costs and benefits of the San Francisco plastic bag ban suggest the health risks they impose are not likely offset by environmental benefits."

J. Klick, J. D. Wright, Grocery Bag Bans and Foodborne Illness, U of Penn, Inst for Law & Econ Research Paper No. 13-2, November 2nd, 2012

I was only able to find this one study on the topic, so more research should be done to be certain. Nevertheless, the findings are alarming. It would appear that banning disposable plastic bags caused a serious health crisis.

The consequences of bag bans can be frightening

Thus, although re-useable bags appear to be the greenest solution by LCA, we need to factor in the safety aspect as well. Such bags would need to be washed after each use, and it is not clear whether they would still be the greener than single-use PE bags when the water and detergent used for washing them is taken into account.

PLASTIC BANKNOTES

Lifecycle analysis is specific to each application of the material. We know that plastics like PE and PP are far superior to paper or cotton when it comes to grocery bags, but we cannot assume that plastic will come out ahead in other applications. Perhaps grocery bags are an exception. The only way to be sure is to look for other applications where paper and plastic compete, so I searched for LCA reports comparing paper and plastic. This revealed two reports on paper banknotes versus plastic notes. It may surprise some people to hear that plastic banknotes have been used widely for decades in several countries. The reports I found online were from the Bank of Canada and the Bank of England.

The Canadian report concluded:

"For all indicators under study (Primary Energy Demand, Global Warming Potential, Eutrophication Potential, Acidification Potential, Smog Potential, human and ecosystem toxicity), most of the impacts are associated with the distribution and use phase. The polymer substrate shows benefits over cotton for all main phases of the life cycle: for the manufacturing phase, since it has to be produced 2.5 fewer times than the cotton paper bank note for the distribution, since it has to be distributed 2.5 less times and its weight is lighter for end-of-life, since the contained carbon in cotton paper bank notes is released as GHG in the landfill."

Life Cycle Assessment of Canada's Polymer Bank Notes and Cotton-Paper Bank Notes - Final Report, C. Marincovic et al., Bank of Canada, Ottawa, ON K1A 0G9 2011

We can see that the polymer (polypropylene) banknotes are clearly superior to cotton because they last much longer.

The Bank of England study concluded:

"When comparing substrates, it is seen that for a given mass of bank notes the paper substrate generally has slightly lower environmental impacts than the polymer substrate. However, because polymer bank notes are assumed to last 2.5 times longer than paper bank notes (the default assumption in this study) a significantly lower mass of polymer bank notes are required to satisfy the functional unit. Hence, overall polymer bank notes have lower environmental impacts than paper bank notes for all impact categories assessed except for photochemical ozone creation potential."

LCA of Paper and Polymer Bank Notes - Final Study Report, P. Shonfield, Bank of England 2013

So, polymer banknotes last 7.5 years in circulation, far longer than a paper banknote, which lasts only three years, and the plastic are far better for the environment. We know with certainty that polymer notes last much longer because they have been in circulation since the 1980s.

THE BEST CHOICE IS THE ONE THAT DOES THE LEAST HARM

Unfortunately, the ideal material doesn't exist. For example, if we start with a natural material like trees, we need to grind them up to make pulp, use nasty chemicals to bleach the pulp, then use a vast amount of water to process the pulp, and so on. In the end, we have paper, but the process to get there places a huge burden on the environment, so it turns out not to be green after all.

Once we realize that there is no perfect material, we see that we need to choose those that do the least harm. Winston Churchill once said:

> "Indeed, it has been said that democracy is the worst form of Government except for all those other forms that have been tried from time to time..."
>
> Sir Winston Churchill

The same can be said for plastics. They are not perfect, but they are the best alternative we have. According to scientific studies, some of the best options include PE, PP, and PET. That's rather fortuitous because they are the most common plastics, and they are among the least expensive as well.

We have all heard the calls to replace plastics. Scientists have looked into the implications of doing just that. They calculated the effects of substituting other materials for plastics packaging and made a report. Here are some of their conclusions:

"Plastic packaging has many properties that are vitally important for packaging applications, including light weight, flexibility, durability, cushioning, and barrier properties, to name a few. This substitution analysis demonstrates that plastic packaging is also an efficient choice in terms of environmental impacts."

"For the six packaging categories analyzed – caps and closures, beverage containers, stretch and shrink film, carrier bags, other rigid packaging, and other flexible packaging – 14.4 million metric tonnes of plastic packaging were used in the US in 2010. If other types of packaging were used to substitute US plastic packaging, more than 64 million metric tonnes of packaging would be required. The substitute packaging would result in significantly higher impacts for all results categories evaluated: total energy demand, expended energy, water consumption, solid waste by weight and by volume, global warming potential, acidification, eutrophication, smog formation, and ozone depletion, as shown previously."

Lifecyle Impacts of Plastic Packaging Compared to Substitutes in the United States and Canada, Franklin Associates, A Division of Eastern Research Group (ERG) 2018

We can see that plastic packaging is by far the best solution. It would take 64 million tons of alternative material to replace 14 million tons of plastic. Another study showed that plastic packaging also leads to enormous reductions in CO_2 emissions because it helps food stay fresh longer. Food production is a major contributor to CO_2 emissions and plastic packaging greatly reduces CO_2, even after accounting for the carbon dioxide from plastics production.

The report also considered electronics, toys, and many other applications for plastics. In every case, switching away from plastics would mean more environmental damage and more end-of-life disposal problems.

Other studies have come to the same conclusions. For example, an Australian study stated:

"If plastic packaging would be substituted by other materials, the respective packaging mass would on average increase by a factor 3.6 life-cycle energy demand would increase by a factor 2.2 or by 1,240 million GJ per year, which is equivalent 27 Mt of crude oil in 106 VLCC tankers or comparable to 20 million heated homes GHG emissions would increase by a factor 2.7 or by 61 million tonnes of CO_2-equivalents per year, comparable to 21 million cars on the road or equivalent to the CO_2-emissions of Denmark."

The impact of plastic packaging on life cycle energy consumption and greenhouse gas emissions in Europe, denkstatt GmbH, July 2011

These researchers conclude that replacing plastic packaging would require vastly more alternative materials, use far more energy, and lead to far more carbon dioxide emissions. The other consequence is that moving away from plastics would generate several-fold more waste. People are quick to point out how much plastic we use and how much waste is generated, but they fail to consider that replacing it creates a problem that is several times worse. Perspective is needed if we are to make sound choices.

SOFT DRINK CONTAINERS

This is a topic that comes up again and again. I see posts online claiming that we need to replace PET with aluminium or glass to save the environment. As always, there was no evidence given, so I decided to look for the evidence.

Franklin Associates did a cradle-to-grave analysis and found that PET was significantly greener in all three categories because it created the least greenhouse gas, used the least energy, and created less waste than either aluminium or glass. The report shows that moving from PET to aluminium would mean double the CO_2, double the waste, and use about 50% more energy usage. Does that sound like a good idea now?

Plastic PET bottle design which uses far too much material

Of course, some products are over-designed and we need to avoid using more material than needed to get the job done.

Container Type	Energy (million BTU)	Solid Waste		Greenhouse Gas (CO$_2$ equivalents)
		Weight (lb)	Volume (yrd³)	
Aluminium Can	16.0	767	0.95	2,766
Glass Bottle	26.6	4,457	2.14	4,848
PET Bottle	11	302	0.67	1,125

Lifecycle inventory of three single-serving soft drink containers, Franklin Associates, August 2009 (figures are per 100,000 ounces of soft drink)

It seems that Coca-Cola has checked their facts, seen the studies, and moved to PET over aluminium cans in order to reduce CO_2 emissions.

SUSTAINABLE BUSINESS   NOVEMBER 6, 2019 / 12:21 PM / A MONTH AGO

Coca-Cola chooses plastic bottle collection over aluminum cans to cut carbon footprint

A review of several such studies conducted by Owen and Boyd highlighted the pros and cons of each material and the variations between each study.

> T. H. Owen & K. Boyd, Beverage Container Review – Final Report, Thompson Rivers University, Office of Environment & Sustainability 2013

In general, PET comes out as having the lowest impact compared to glass and aluminium, especially when it is recycled and when larger containers are used.

CONCLUSIONS

In general, it turns out that plastic is a much better choice than cotton, metal, glass and usually paper. The main factor is weight—that is, for a given application, far less plastic is needed than wood, paper, glass, or metal to do the same job.

As a rule of thumb, to know which solution makes sense, just weigh the items and compare. A plastic straw weighs 1g whereas a paper straw weighs 2g. Plus, a plastic straw can be used many times and a paper straw barely works once. A plastic Kroger grocery bag weighs less than 6g but a paper Kroger bag weighs 60g. The paper bag is far less green according to LCA and generates 10x more waste. In the next chapter, we will take a closer look at waste.

Lie #1 – Paper, cotton, glass, and metal are greener than plastics.

Truth – Common plastics like PE, PP and PET are the best choices according to multiple independent lifecycle analyses from all around the world. Replacing plastic leads to far more material used, more energy consumed, more waste, and more CO_2.

CHAPTER TWO
WASTE

WASTE – PAST, PRESENT, FUTURE

When presented with the facts and the many lifecycle analyses on materials, people usually see that plastics are actually the preferred solution. They then ask, "What about all the waste and the litter?" We hear a lot about these topics, and rightly so. Let us once again look at the best available data to see what we can learn about waste. What lessons can we learn from the past? How much waste is there today and what is it made up of? What can be done to reduce waste?

HISTORICAL PERSPECTIVE

In 1880, there were over one-hundred-and-fifty-thousand horses living in New York, each creating over twenty pounds of manure a day. That translates to forty-five thousand tons a month of horse excrement. The streets were covered, and the smell was horrific. This was not isolated to New York. In London, it was estimated that fifty years into the future the whole city would be buried under nine feet of manure. Back in New York, this inspired architects to create the Brownstone buildings whereby the front door is elevated far above street level to avoid unpleasant odours.

Hosed - Is there a quick fix for the climate?, Elizabeth Kolbert,
The New Yorker, November 8th, 2009

This is only one instance of a major environmental crisis. Regulatory solutions were discussed but, in the end, electrification of public transportation and the adoption of the automobile quickly solved the problem. The point is that the developed world has had huge environmental problems in the past. Some were solved by technology, as with the horse example above. Others were solved by aggressive regulation; for example, the infamous Great Smog of London that killed thousands of people in the early 1950s.

The Great Smog of London Wikipedia entry

Is it so surprising that developing countries have similar issues now to the ones we had just a few decades ago? I would say not. They have major problems with litter because they do not yet have regulations in place, nor do they have the collection and disposal infrastructure. It appears to be human nature to act only when the conditions become unbearable, and that is starting to happen in many parts of the world.

THE PRESENT

Let us look at how waste has grown over the years and how the introduction of plastic has influenced it.

The EPA (US Environmental Protection Agency) records the amount of household waste produced per year, so accurate records exist and are available to the public. There is so much data that I had an independent data expert put it in a manageable form. We found a steady growth of US waste over the last several decades. There was virtually no plastic to begin with because it was a new type of material, but then it became more prevalent as time went on. Plastic is a relatively small fraction of overall waste, which is surprising given that virtually every newspaper article and online post talks about plastic as if it were the number one cause of waste. Instead, the data shows that plastic became the 4th most common type of waste and has remained in that position for decades. We can conclude that plastic is not the most pressing problem and that it is not taking over as the environmentalists tell us.

What else can we see from the EPA data? The amount of trash (the EPA call it municipal solid waste, or MSW for short) increases as the population increases. That comes as no surprise. A closer look at the data, however, shows that the rate at which waste increased has actually declined. That means that something has happened to help us reduce waste generation per person over recent years.

This was investigated by scientists in a peer-reviewed article. They found that plastics are responsible for the reduction in our creation of waste:

"A comparison of waste generation rates for each material category found in MSW reveals that plastics increased by nearly 84 times from 1960 to 2013 while total MSW increased only 2.9 times. The increase in plastic waste generation coincides with a decrease in glass and metal found in the MSW stream. In addition, calculating the material substitution rates for glass, metal and other materials with plastics in packaging and containers demonstrates an overall reduction by weight and by volume in MSW generation of approximately 58% over the same time period."

D. A. Tsiamis, M. Torres, M. J. Castaldi, Role of plastics in decoupling municipal solid waste and economic growth in the U.S., Waste Management, 77, 147-155 2018

They conclude that plastic dramatically reduced the amount of municipal solid waste (MSW). This is in line with the other studies that found replacing plastics would lead to far more material usage, waste, and environmental burden. I have seen endless posts where people ask us to replace plastic with some other material such as paper, metal, or glass, but the science clearly shows that we need 3-4 pounds of material to replace just one pound of plastic. Who in their right mind would propose generating 3-4x more waste?

This is the kind of insanity that results from taking action before checking the facts. It is exactly the sort of nonsensical knee-jerk reaction that I hope we can avoid after people have read this book.

This data may also explain why the public believe that plastic waste is a problem when in reality, it is not. The public has seen the amount of plastic waste increase 84x over the last several decades. It must look as though it is mushrooming out of control. And yet, what the public does not realize is that the increased use of plastic has dramatically lowered the amount of paper, cardboard, and other materials. It's ironic that the more plastic we see, the worse it appears but the better it actually is for the environment. Appearances can deceive us, which is why we need hard data to be sure of the facts.

An in-depth analysis has been performed to estimate the impact of replacing plastic. Here is an excerpt from that report:

"For the six packaging categories analyzed – caps and closures, beverage containers, stretch and shrink film, carrier bags, other rigid packaging, and other flexible packaging – 14.4 million metric tonnes of plastic packaging were used in the US in 2010. If other types of packaging were used to substitute US plastic packaging, more than 64 million metric tonnes of packaging would be required... [...] energy demand and result in [...] more global warming potential impacts, expressed as CO₂ equivalents, compared to the equivalent plastic packaging."

Impact of Plastics Packaging on Life Cycle Energy Consumption & Greenhouse Gas Emissions in the United States and Canada – Substitution Analysis, Franklin Associates, A Division of Eastern Research Group (ERG), January 2014

The study showed that replacing plastic packaging in the US would mean adding 50 million tons more material, leading to 50 million tons more waste every year. Does that sound green to you? It would be a spectacularly stupid thing to do, and yet, yielding to pressure from us, the customers, companies like the supermarkets Iceland and Waitrose and other companies like Nestlé, IHG, and Etihad Airlines are doing just that. Companies are listening to the demands of the public, but those demands are based on misinformation. Be careful what you wish for is a saying that applies well here. Right now, we are wishing for 50 million tons more waste, 80% higher energy usage, and double the CO_2.

J. Zheng, S. Suh, Strategies to reduce the global carbon footprint of plastics, Nature Climate Change, 9, p 374–378 2019

We noted earlier that waste grows with population. When I was at school, we were taught that the world's population was exploding, and a crisis was coming as the population spiralled out of control. However, as we know now, that has not happened. We reached the maximum rate of population growth many years ago and it has been slowing ever since. It turns out that poor countries have more children, but as they climb out of poverty there is no need for large families and effective birth control brings the population growth down dramatically. This is important because as each country gets out of poverty, the waste problem will decline as their ability to manage their waste improves. There has been tremendous progress in reducing global poverty; you can see compelling data in books such as Factfulness by Hans Rosling and Enlightenment Now by Steven Pinker. We can safely expect that the global waste problem will be mitigated by more moderate population growth.

Now that we have seen that plastics are not the primary contributor to waste and that waste is not growing out of control, it seems like a good idea to see which materials are causing waste.

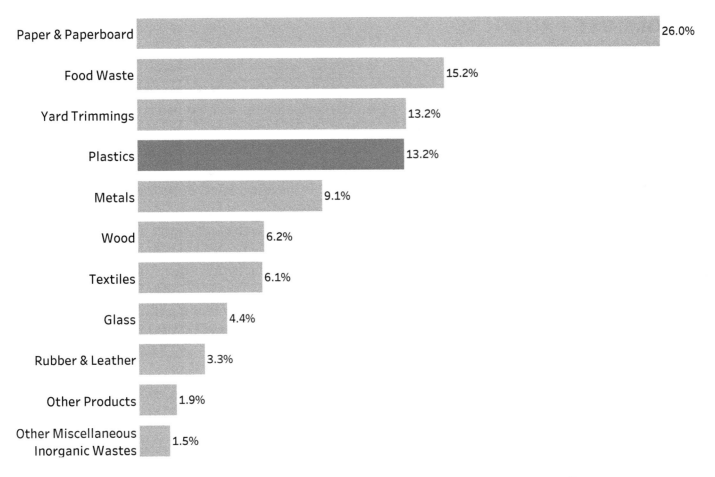

Paper & Paperboard — 26.0%
Food Waste — 15.2%
Yard Trimmings — 13.2%
Plastics — 13.2%
Metals — 9.1%
Wood — 6.2%
Textiles — 6.1%
Glass — 4.4%
Rubber & Leather — 3.3%
Other Products — 1.9%
Other Miscellaneous Inorganic Wastes — 1.5%

Source: www.epa.gov

The first thing that leapt out to me was that paper and cardboard are by far the largest culprits when it comes to waste. Why then is all the media attention, all the attention from green groups, and all the public scrutiny focused on plastics, which are tied for third place? Surely, if we want to make the biggest impact, we should be looking at the major source of waste. We could ask ourselves how it came to be that the truth is so very different than the narrative we are fed. We will address that topic later in the book. You may be thinking that we need not be concerned with paper, cardboard, food waste, and yard trimmings because they are degradable and plastics are not. Actually, that turns out to be a fallacy as well, and we will cover it later on.

SINGLE-USE PRODUCTS

Single-use products are under intense scrutiny, and rightly so. Although we probably don't want to be reusing plastic syringes in hospitals, there are plenty of products where single-use is not a wise approach.

How did single-use come into existence? It is made possible only when materials become so inexpensive that we can afford to discard them without a second thought—or a second use. Think of the lollipop sticks, newspapers, candy wrappers, and water bottles we have become accustomed to discarding. I would argue that some of these items do not have to be single-use. What do I mean by that? Well, for example, one of my daughters likes to drink her water through a straw at night. We all know that the single-use plastic straw is notorious. However, it turns out that a plastic straw does not have to be thrown away after one use. After all, who is forcing us to use these products only once? She reused the same (rinsed) plastic water straw for three months and it was still in pristine condition. Reusing it 100x drastically lowers the environmental impact of the straw. Of course, we now know that a paper straw is less green, generates more waste, and barely survives one use, let alone a hundred. The best option, though, is to take no straw at all.

Single-use sounds like the ultimate example of wastage, doesn't it? After all, what could be worse than single-use? I'll tell you what! Zero-use! I get over a pound a day of zero-use paper shoved in my letterbox and thrown on my driveway! I get fliers, brochures, magazines I never ordered, catalogues, and even a hefty newspaper I didn't ask for. It is all zero-use because it goes directly into the trash can. We just saw from the EPA data that paper is the number one cause of waste, and it's obvious that zero-use is worse than single-use. It therefore boggles my mind that no one is talking about all the paper junk we have delivered to our doorsteps every day. The problem is far worse than it is for plastics, and yet we hear not one word about it. It's shocking, and there is no way to stop it. It's relentless. To put it in perspective, a plastic straw weighs 0.5g, yet I received 600g of spam paper today alone. That paper weighs as much as 1,000 plastic straws or 100 plastic bags. Why is it that people are obsessed with plastic straws when 1,000x more paper is delivered every day to our houses?

Please note that this is not an attempt to defend the use of plastic. All waste is undesirable. Rather, the point is that if we are to attack the waste problem, why overlook the major problem and devote all of our attention and effort to a lesser issue? There should be a way to report this senseless destruction of trees and our environment. There should be fines and jail time for repeat offenders. I hope we can pass laws against automated delivery of litter to our driveways and junk to our mailboxes. The impact would be instantaneous and huge.

The book Rubbish! The Archaeology of Garbage points out that removal of plastics from landfills would not solve anything, as plastic occupies just 16% of landfill space by volume. It turns out that humans are not good at estimating where the real problems lie. For example, there is a lot of talk about disposable diapers as a huge problem when, in actuality, they account for less than 2% of the space in a landfill. Similarly, plastic bottles take up less than 1% of landfill space. Instead, they point to paper and construction debris as the main culprits, which combine to account for well over half of US refuse. They say that these are the two big ticket items we should be focussing on.

William L. Rathje, Cullen Murphy, Rubbish!: The Archaeology of Garbage, HarperCollins 1992

The cardboard & paper industry creates most waste but is hiding from scrutiny

I recently discovered that the single-use problem is not new. In fact, it has been around for several thousand years. It is always presented a modern-day invention, but the evidence says otherwise:

3,600-year-old disposable cup shows even our ancestors hated doing dishes

3,600-year-old disposable cup shows even our ancestors hated doing dishes, Amy Woodyatt, CNN December 16th 2019

"People may be very surprised to know that disposable, single-use cups are not the invention of our modern consumerist society, but in fact can be traced back thousands of years. Three-and-a-half-thousand years ago, the Minoans were using them for a very similar reason to us today: to serve drinks at parties. The only difference is the material."

The difference was that in those days, they cast aside clay drinking cups which have clearly survived for thousands of years because they are being discovered today. In contrast, a cup disposed of today is made of paper or plastic and will degrade in just a few years of exposure outdoors. More about that later.

MINIMIZING WASTE

All living things create waste. Every breath we take leads to an outward breath of waste gases. Other bodily functions create waste too. There is no avoiding waste entirely, as anyone who has attempted to hold their breath will know. Civilization has simply created new kinds of waste, and we need to adapt in order to minimize it, just as we did in the past for horse manure and smog. One way to reduce waste is to reuse materials so they have a longer useful life. Another way is to recycle materials so they can become new products, thereby extending their life.

RECYCLING

One frequent criticism of plastics is that they are not recycled enough. Lifecycle analysis tells us that recycling plastics is good for the environment, so why isn't it done more? Once again, it is time to check the data to see what it reveals.

Waste Management by Materials, Recycled, Landfilled, Combusted

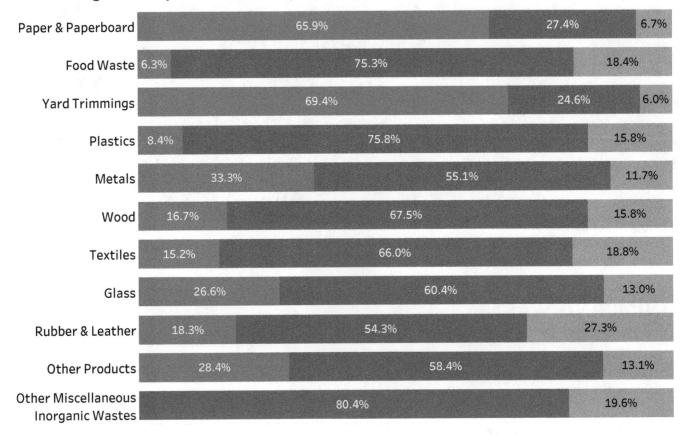

Material	Recycled	Landfilled	Combusted
Paper & Paperboard	65.9%	27.4%	6.7%
Food Waste	6.3%	75.3%	18.4%
Yard Trimmings	69.4%	24.6%	6.0%
Plastics	8.4%	75.8%	15.8%
Metals	33.3%	55.1%	11.7%
Wood	16.7%	67.5%	15.8%
Textiles	15.2%	66.0%	18.8%
Glass	26.6%	60.4%	13.0%
Rubber & Leather	18.3%	54.3%	27.3%
Other Products	28.4%	58.4%	13.1%
Other Miscellaneous Inorganic Wastes		80.4%	19.6%

Source: www.epa.gov

In the USA, only 9% of plastic is recycled at present. It is a low percentage, but that's also the case with several other popular materials. Looking at plastics, though, there is no denying that the number should be higher. What prevents more recycling of plastics?

A lot of misinformation has been spread on this topic. As one example, we are told to avoid black plastics because they cannot be recycled. But is that true? As a plastic materials expert, I can explain. Black plastics are actually easy to recycle. You simply melt them and make a new part. Where's the problem, then? The issue is with sorting. To recycle plastics, you first need to sort them, so that you recycle PE waste together with only PE waste, PP waste with PP waste, and so on. It is harder to sort conventional black plastics automatically because the machines that check the type of plastic work based on light, so they don't work properly on black parts which absorb all the light. So, instead of telling us that, we are told the lie that they cannot be recycled. What it really comes down to is that the recycler doesn't want to go to the extra effort to recycle black plastic. This kind of lie confuses and misleads the public. Even more worrying is that the solution to the problem of sorting black plastic has been on the market for several years. By using a different kind of black colourant, the machines are able to sort the parts without difficulty. Nowadays, there really is no reason not to recycle black plastic, and yet this misinformation persists.

You may think that is an isolated case, but it is not. In Ohio, school children are taught that containers whose opening is wider than their base cannot be recycled. I was really surprised when my kids came home and told me that because I know it's not true. Plastic can be ground up, remelted, and recycled no matter what shape it is. So, I searched on Google, and sure enough, only in Ohio do they tell people that such containers cannot be recycled. Here is what we are told online:

> The following items are not currently accepted through this recycling program
>
> Plastic: Containers that DO NOT have a bottle neck or a base larger than the top. For example, yogurt cups, butter tubs, drinking cups, plastic plates, cups, clamshell containers, plastic bags, foam packaging, bubble wrap, and plastic utensils.

https://www.swaco.org

The rest of the country has no problem with such containers but in Ohio, the children are taught these items are "unrecyclable".

PLASTIC RESIN IDENTIFICATION CODES

PETE	HDPE	PVC	LDPE	PP	PS	OTHER
Polyethylene Terephthalate	High Density Polyethylene	Polyvinyl Chloride	Low Density Polyethylene	Polypropylene	Polystyrene	Other
Recyclable	Recyclable	Recyclable at specialist points	Recyclable at specialist points	Recyclable	Recyclable at specialist points	Not easily recyclable

* Check with your local recycling program to confirm which materials are accepted in the recycling bin or at a special drop-off or collection program.

Most plastics can be recycled if the right facilities are present

In general, most plastics are rather easy to recycle. You need to sort them by type, grind them up, and then remelt them into new shapes. This takes very little energy and recycling can be done many times with little or no loss in properties. Why doesn't the public know this? This is what we should teach children in school because it's true. The plastic types one through six can all be recycled by melting, and together they account for 87% of plastics (see the diagram Market share of commodity plastics in Chapter 4).

So, from a technical perspective, there is no reason not to recycle far more than we do now in the US. We know it's the green choice, and we know it's possible because several other countries have been doing it for years. If we look at the data for Europe, for example, we see that every country is far ahead of the US. In Europe, the average recycling rate is ~45% and is as high as 75% in Lithuania. This is a clear indication that the USA has chosen to fall behind by not making the appropriate investments in recycling infrastructure.

Plastic waste and the recycling myth, Katharina Wecker, DW 12th October 2018

Plastics are very sensitive to contamination, which is an impediment to recycling. It means that they must be washed properly and then sorted with great accuracy. PE must be recycled only together with other PE of the same type, PP must be mixed only with PP, and so on. The reason is that plastics are immiscible with each other, so when you melt a mixture of two or more plastics, you get droplets of one plastic inside the other one. It's like the emulsion you get when you shake oil and water together. Those droplets of plastic can dramatically lower the mechanical properties of the material, especially the impact resistance. Thankfully, there are compounds called compatibilizers that act like surfactants to can help improve the properties of immiscible plastics.

You may be wondering why the government or companies don't simply install more sorting and recycling facilities. Surely, that would make great business sense. Unfortunately, this not the case. If there was money to be made, you can be sure that it would be more popular. It turns out that recycled plastic is often more expensive than new, virgin material. In such cases, recycled plastic is hard to sell. Often the recycled material is discoloured, so you can't make vibrant, attractive colours out of it. Imagine you start with grey water. No matter how much pigment you put in it, you can't make the water an intense colour. Companies ask for recycled material only to find it's more expensive and often looks unappealing. It may be that in the future, customers must become accustomed to less vibrant packaging.

DESIGN FOR RECYCLING

There are three main actions that we can take to improve recyclability:

1. Try to make each product from one material because mixtures of plastics do not recycle as easily
2. Make everything possible from just three plastics (PE, PP or PET) in order to simplify sorting and recycling
3. Make the plastic materials more durable so they can be recycled more times before losing too much strength

I have spent my career working for and with major corporations. I know that competition is intense and that the difference between profit and loss can be a penny here or there in your production and materials costs. At present, products are designed to be as cheap as possible. You may not be aware that over the last few decades, plastic packaging has become thinner and thinner. We use 30% less now than we used to, and it's still decreasing year over year. Every conference I attend focusses on downgauging (making plastic films thinner) and lightweighting (where we make automotive parts lighter for better fuel efficiency). These are industry megatrends which help reduce material use and, in that way, help the environment.

The drive for the lowest possible cost can also have negative effects, however. Designing to be cheap means not maximizing durability. Sometimes parts are made so thin that they are too weak and fail. What is more common is a failure to add enough stabilizers to protect the plastic for the long term. There is a false narrative that plastics last forever, but nothing could be further from the truth. The main plastics in use today are PE and PP. Although they are the greenest choices, these plastics are chemically unstable and can only be used because we add stabilizers that protect them when they are molten during processing and then later on in use. Without stabilizers, they simply degrade and become useless. Polypropylene is the worst example, as it loses strength in just one year at room temperature unless protective additives are used.

At present, companies select the cheapest stabilizers and use as little as possible to protect the product for its intended lifespan. Why are they so frugal? It all comes down to cost. Fierce competition means there is no scope to add more cost than is absolutely necessary. This means that products don't last as long as they could. More importantly, it means that when it comes time to recycle the plastic, the stabilizer is all used up, so that reheating the plastic causes unacceptable degradation, leading to discolouration and loss of physical strength. There is much more about additives later on in the book.

If we are to design for recyclability, then we need to select better stabilizers and use more of them. If we do that, then plastics like PE and PP can be recycled many times without loss in properties. That has already been demonstrated, so it is not mere speculation. This is the way forward.

REUSE

Reusing items is a green alternative to simply throwing them away. Reuse also means generating less waste, as each product remains deployed for longer, thereby delaying disposal. Many of the items we use today don't need to be thrown away. I already gave the example of plastic straws, which can be rinsed or put in the dishwasher and used a hundred times or more. Another example is the PET bottles that sport drinks come in. These are sturdy and can be reused countless times for water or other drinks. The term "single-use" is misleading because it makes it sound as though the item can and should be used only one time. The reality is that we, the customer, can choose whether we want to discard perfectly serviceable items, or do the responsible thing and reuse them until they can no longer function.

REDUCE

Speaking of straws, in most cases, there's no need to give one and no need to accept one. Simply drink out of a cup, unless you have special needs. The same goes for other items. We live in a world where a huge marketing engine makes us crave the latest phone, even though we know our existing phone is just fine. We are told to buy new clothes in the colours and fabrics that are deemed "in" for that season. This way of thinking needs to be adjusted with the environment in mind.

The public doesn't realize it, but plastic packaging has become thinner and thinner over the years, substantially reducing the amount used per item.

"Initial thicknesses of plastic packaging material averaged approximately one-third of the weight of the combined glass and metal replacement until the year 2000. Starting in 2000, the plastic packaging continuously decreased by about 3% per year, further reducing the weight exchanged until the ratio reached one quarter of the combined replacement weight (Franklin Associates, 2014)."

The use of plastics over time has been monitored, so we can tell how much progress has been made over the decades.

"...according to the British Plastics Federation's database, between 1970 and 1990 the weight of the average plastic yoghurt pot decreased from 12 g to 5 g, and the corresponding decrease in weight of a typical plastics detergent bottle was from 300 g to 100 g. Similarly, typical general purpose and industrial plastic films, bags and sacks have decreased in average thickness by up to 400% over the same time interval. As a consequence of these improvements in functional weight characteristics, plastics transportation costs and associated emissions have been reduced dramatically."

T.J. O'Neill, Life Cycle Assessment and Environmental Impact of Polymeric Products, RAPRA Reviews 2003

The same RAPRA report noted that as the use of plastics in cars dramatically increased, the gasoline consumption of those cars decreased by 14%. Plastics are, of course, considerably lighter than the materials they replace.

Although plastic can be used in extremely low amounts, it is up to designers to optimize the design. I have held PET water bottles so thin that you could barely touch them without crushing them. That is efficient design. On the other hand, we are all familiar with the PET sport drink bottles that are so thick you wonder if they are meant to be used on the battlefield. The two designs perform the same function, but the over-designed bottle is made to impress and conveys a certain high-quality brand image. It probably does impress certain customers, but we need to retrain ourselves to respect and admire the minimalist approach. It leads to far more efficient use of our resources and far less waste. We need to retrain ourselves not to demand fancy packaging.

CONCLUSIONS

The public believes that plastics are the main cause of waste and that the problem is spiralling out of control. However, looking at the facts tells a very different story.

We know that plastics are nowhere near the main cause of waste and that our use of plastics has substantially reduced overall waste creation. Furthermore, studies show that replacing plastic would mean creating 3-4x more waste on average, and that would be a supremely unwise decision. The data shows that the number one problem is paper and cardboard, which utterly dominate our waste problem and yet almost no attention is given to that topic. It must be the world's best-kept secret. Worse still, much of the paper waste is zero-use in the form of fliers, newspapers, and catalogues that go directly into the trash can.

If we want to address waste, then first we need to recognize that plastics are helping us reduce waste. Then we need to focus on the materials that dominate the waste stream, including paper, cardboard, and lawn trimmings. We need public pressure for strict laws against delivery of zero-use products, with harsh fines for violators.

Waste is an unavoidable consequence of the industrialization that has dramatically improved our quality of life, but there is still much we can do to reduce it. Inevitably, some waste will be mismanaged and become litter or pollution. These are topics we will cover next.

Lie #2 – Plastics are the cause of our waste problem.

Truth – Plastics account for 13% of waste, they reduce overall waste, and replacing them would lead to three or four times more waste.

CHAPTER THREE LITTER

LITTER – SOURCES AND SOLUTIONS

This section considers litter, including what it is, what causes it, and what we can do to prevent it. As with any topic, checking the facts first allows us to identify the true problem, which is vital for crafting an effective solution.

PERCEPTION

In 1880, there were over one-hundred-and-fifty-thousand horses living in New York, each creating over twenty pounds of manure a day. That translates to forty-five thousand tons a month of horse excrement. The streets were covered, and the smell was horrific. This was not isolated to New York. In London, it was estimated that fifty years into the future the whole city would be buried under nine feet of manure. Back in New York, this inspired architects to create the Brownstone buildings whereby the front door is elevated far above street level to avoid unpleasant odours.

Hosed - Is there a quick fix for the climate?, Elizabeth Kolbert,
The New Yorker, November 8th, 2009

Before we proceed, I have a confession to make. To me, one of the ugliest things I know of is a plastic grocery bag. Just one bag on the kitchen counter and the whole kitchen is an eyesore. And this from a plastics expert! I can't even work out why it's so ugly, but there seems to be a keen response. Interestingly, I once read a book that pointed out that, technically speaking, a felled sequoia is litter.

They had a picture of a huge sequoia on the forest floor, and they even noted that such dead trees have remained intact for at least 500 years with hardly any degradation (Scott, 1999). That's tons and tons of material that doesn't readily degrade, and yet it evokes no negative response when I see that image. In fact, it looks natural and even majestic. My eye accepts that image without issue, and yet, one tiny plastic bag and I'm on edge.

Gerald Scott, Polymers and the Environment, RSC Paperbacks Page 97 1999

I looked into this and found that people favour natural-looking images over man-made ones (Kardan, 2015). Perhaps we're programmed to spot objects that don't belong, as a survival mechanism. That's not my area of expertise, but it may be part of our response to certain objects like plastic straws and bags. In contrast, plastic timber has not caused any outcry with the public. It looks natural like wood, so no one has a problem with it.

O. Kardan et al., Is the preference of natural versus man-made scenes driven by bottom–up processing of the visual features of nature? Front. Psychol. 6:471 2015

Another issue facing plastic litter is how much visual space it occupies. For example, a standard US grocery bag weighs 5.5g but it looks huge to the human eye. What we perceive is a large amount of litter, when the actual weight of that litter is the same a one US quarter coin, a wine cork, a gaming die, or one blackberry. This optical illusion is a large part of the reason for the unjustified attacks on plastic. We think the problem is a lot worse than it really is. It is estimated that 2% of all plastic produced is littered, and there is much room for improvement as certain regions catch up with the best-in-class countries.

J. R. Jambeck, Plastic waste inputs from land into the ocean, Science 347 (6223), 768-771, 2015

The perceived amount of litter is huge, but the actual amount of litter is much less. This is represented by the weight of a plastic bag compared to a plastic gaming die, which is just 18mm, or 0.7 inches, across.

Another material that suffers from this effect is expanded polystyrene. One expanded PS packing noodle weighs just 0.07g, so 80 of them take up a lot of volume but weigh only as much as one bag or gaming die.

Plastic grocery bag and gaming die drawn to scale (same weight of plastic)

THE TRUE CAUSE OF LITTER

The Meriam Webster Dictionary defines litter as a noun and a verb...

Litter as a noun: "trash, wastepaper, or garbage lying scattered about"

Litter as a verb: "to strew with scattered articles"

Litterer or litterbug: "one who litters a public area"

From this, we understand what litter is and how it got there. Clearly, litter is defined as objects scattered around and/or created by the action of a litterer. Litter is certainly not made up of objects that spring to life and scatter themselves. When I take a walk outside and see a candy wrapper or a soda can, I know immediately that it was left there by an irresponsible person, namely a litterer, and I conjure up vivid imaginings of punishments for the culprit. Somehow, in recent years, it has become commonplace to discuss litter as though the material itself were somehow to blame. We are presented with a picture of litter on a beach along with a headline telling us to be "tough on plastics". No one seems to question it, and yet, when you stop to think about it, we all know that the cola can, newspaper, or grocery bag cannot be blamed. It is both naïve and counterproductive to blame objects or materials for the actions of irresponsible human beings. Only by correct placement of the blame can we take appropriate and effective action. Once we realize that people are the problem, then we recognize that altering human behaviour must be the solution. Fortunately, we all know how to encourage proper behaviour. We educate our children, and for adults, we give encouragements for good behaviour and punishments for bad. If it were up to me, there would be heavy, escalating fines and community service for litterers.

CAUSE

EFFECT

People are the cause and litter is the effect

PROOF THAT HUMAN BEHAVIOUR CAUSES LITTER

I know that some people will probably refute the claim that litter is a people problem. So, I created a couple of examples that I would like to share.

Let us imagine you are driving your car. It has 300,000 miles on it, and it finally stops working in the middle of the road. You get out and leave the car there to rust away. It is now a huge piece of worthless litter creating an unsightly mess in the environment. Who created that situation? Is the litter (i.e., the car) to blame? Most people would readily admit that the car cannot take the blame. I contend that it is exactly the same situation with every piece of litter, whether it's a car, a cigarette butt or a candy wrapper. Every piece was left there by a human being. Blaming plastics for litter is equivalent to driving your car into a tree and blaming the car. It's human nature to shift the blame, but that doesn't make it right. Until we face that harsh reality, there will be no progress with our litter problem. This leads me to a related topic. I always see people blaming Coca-Cola or Unilever for litter. How unjust! In the example above, would you blame Ford or Volvo for abandoning your car? Would you demand that they pick it up and recycle it? No! Why then do people demand that Nestlé come to pick up candy wrappers?

An abandoned car – who would expect the manufacturer to pick it up?

Here is an even more powerful example to show that people cause litter. It's estimated that 162 billion new banknotes go into circulation every year. Ninety-five per cent of those are paper and the rest are made of plastic. That means about eight billion new plastic notes are issued per year, which means about one plastic banknote per year for each person on Earth. It's a truly gargantuan number, but how many of those "make their way" into the oceans or wash up on beaches? How many of those eight billion banknotes do we see on the street or pavement when we go for a walk? That's right. None! They have been around since 1996, so we should be drowning in plastic banknote "litter" by now. If using materials like paper or plastic was the real cause of litter, we would see banknotes everywhere. In reality, we see none because people choose to take care of their banknotes, whether they be paper or plastic.

Explainer: what's all the fuss about polymer banknotes?
Mark Harding Chemistry World Magazine, RSC, 13th September 2016

Eight billion PP banknotes printed per year – how many have you seen as litter?

The same argument can be applied to credit cards. They are small, easily misplaced pieces of plastic. According to the latest figures, each American adult carries more than two credit cards on average. That translates to over 300 million plastic cards all around the country. When was the last time you saw one on the sidewalk? When is the last time one washed up on the beach when you were on holiday? Do we see them clogging our rivers and sewers? We do not. These ubiquitous pieces of small plastic do not sprout legs or flippers and "make their way" into the environment. People act responsibly with these small pieces of plastic. The message could not be clearer: people cause litter.

These examples also lead us to an effective and proven way to solve the litter crisis. As long as plastic is cheap, people drop it, but when it is a banknote worth just $1, then they never drop it. Even if a note is dropped on occasion, it is immediately picked up. We see that plastic articles with value are "self-tidying". This explains why the PET bottle return system in Norway works so well. They have a PET bottle return rate of 97% because each bottle has a small deposit associated with it. In Norway, each bottle is recycled twelve times on average, making the whole system very friendly indeed because recycling bottles is greener than making new ones. It uses less material, less energy, and creates less carbon dioxide. Norway has led the way, and other countries are now considering a similar system having seen the success of the Norwegians. We should always be on the lookout for new approaches in other countries so that we can copy them once they are proven to work.

Science & Environment

UK 'could adopt' Norway bottle recycling system

By Roger Harrabin
BBC environment analyst

UK 'could adopt' Norway bottle recycling system, Roger Harrabin, BBC News 7th February 2018

OCEAN LITTER

It is well documented that marine wildlife is affected by plastic objects. For example, animals can become entangled in nets. Some animals eat plastic, and although the material is non-toxic, they may suffer other effects. For example, eating inert material can take up space in the stomach, giving the sensation of being full but without any calorific value (although an animal would have to eat a lot of plastic for that to happen). Another effect is when animals ingest plastic and it gets stuck in their throats, stomachs, or gastrointestinal tract, leading to injury or death.

J. G.B. Derraik, The pollution of the marine environment by plastic debris: a review, Marine Pollution Bulletin, 44(9), 842-852 2002

These effects are real, they are significant in magnitude, and they do need to be addressed. However, we need to recognize that all of this damage happens because plastic and other articles are in places where they should not be. There would be no problem at all if people were not intentionally dumping plastic and other waste into the oceans. The problem is clearly not with plastic itself, but with the unconscionable behaviour of some humans who are littering up our oceans. We will look at that in more detail next.

Marine Anthropogenic Litter, M. Bergmann, L. Gutow, M. Klages (Eds.) Springer, Berlin, 2015

THE GREAT PACIFIC GARBAGE PATCH

The ocean currents can form a vortex that traps any litter floating on the water. This has been the subject of much attention because the patches are so large. One such patch is estimated to hold 80,000 tons of mixed plastic.

Great Pacific Garbage Patch

The Great Pacific Garbage Patch is a collection of marine debris in the North Pacific Ocean. Marine debris is litter that ends up in the ocean, seas, and other large bodies of water.

National Geographic – Resource Library Encyclopedic Entry

The gyres are often described as floating islands of plastic, which conjures up a powerful image. But the image is a false one:

"Despite the common public perception of the patch existing as giant islands of floating garbage, its low density (four particles per cubic meter) prevents detection by satellite imagery, or even by casual boaters or divers in the area. This is because the patch is a widely dispersed area consisting primarily of suspended 'fingernail-sized or smaller bits of plastic,' often microscopic, particles in the upper water column."

What is the Great Pacific Garbage Patch? National Ocean Service
Great Pacific garbage patch – Wikipedia

You read that correctly, the so-called plastic islands are invisible from space and you can't tell they are there, even if you are swimming in one. Once again, we have been misled into picturing a catastrophic image when the truth is very different.

Another aspect worth considering is the density of plastics. Plastics tend to be light materials, for example PE and PP both float on water. That is why we see mainly plastics floating whereas other materials like metal, glass, ceramics and even some types of wood, sink. The plastic is visible, so it draws our attention. In contrast, the other materials all sink, so we don't give them a second thought — out of sight, out of mind.

WHAT'S IN THE PATCH?

Almost half of it is discarded fishing nets and most of the rest is other fishing industry gear, such as ropes, oyster spacers, eel traps, crates, and baskets. This was a surprise to the scientists who went out to study it.

The Great Pacific Garbage Patch Isn't What You Think it Is

It's not all bottles and straws—the patch is mostly abandoned fishing gear.

The Great Pacific Garbage Patch Isn't What You Think it Is - It's not all bottles and straws—the patch is mostly abandoned fishing gear, Laura Parker, National Geographic, March 22nd 2018

So, if it is mostly fishing gear, how did it get there?

WHO'S AT FAULT?

It is amazing to me that somehow plastics take the blame for the gyres when they are clearly the fault of the fishing industry. I bet if there was a $50,000 dollar fine for returning to harbour without your net, this problem would vanish pretty quickly. Perhaps governments should order fishing boats to go out and get these nets, because fishing boats put them there. Perhaps there needs to be a redesign of the nets so that they are not so easily lost.

40 Tons of Fishing Nets Pulled From Great Pacific Garbage Patch

40 Tons of Fishing Nets Pulled from Great Pacific Garbage Patch, Olga R. Rodriguez, Associated Press June 28th, 2019

This Time Magazine article about a boat that had recovered 40 tons of nets was supposed to be uplifting news, but then I checked to see how much was dumped per year. It was reported that in 1975 alone, the world's fishing fleet dumped approximately 135,400 tons of plastic fishing gear and 23,600 tons of synthetic packaging material into the sea.

J. G. B. Derraik, The pollution of the marine environment by plastic debris: a review, Marine Pollution Bulletin 44, 842–852 2002

Clearly, removing 40 tons is not really going to make a dent, not as long as the fishing industry is not held accountable and not as long as they continue to behave in an irresponsible, reprehensible manner.

M. Cawthorn, Impacts of marine debris on wildlife in New Zealand coastal waters, Proceedings of Marine Debris in New Zealand's Coastal Waters Workshop, 9th March 1989, Wellington, New Zealand. Department of Conservation, Wellington, New Zealand, pp. 5–6 1989

We have been led to believe that the problem of plastics in the ocean is ever increasing. However, that is not the case. A very detailed study over 60 years showed that the entanglement of animals in plastic nets did increase from the 1950s onward and peaked in the 2000s, but has since begun to decrease.

C. Ostle & R. C. Thompson et al., Rate of added microplastic decreased over time: The rise in ocean plastics evidenced from a 60-year time series, Nature Communications, 10:1622 2019

The press always tells us about all the plastic that "makes its way to the sea". None of that plastic grew legs or flippers. All of the litter in our waters is preventable and is not a necessary consequence of using plastic. It is important to recognize that these nets do cause real, measurable damage to wildlife that becomes entangled. Nets are designed to trap things, and I am sure that the pre-plastic rope nets did the same thing. These days, nets happen to be made of plastic and somehow plastic is assigned the blame, but it is the fishermen who should be taking the flak for this disaster. If you are angry at the harm done to wildlife, then I suggest you campaign for heavy fines and jail time for the offenders.

WHAT ABOUT THE TURTLES?

We cannot avoid the infamous image of a sea turtle with a "plastic straw" up its nose. That was a very disturbing video, and I can understand why anyone with any empathy at all was moved by it. Appealing to people's emotions is a powerful way to get attention and action, and it certainly worked in this case. However, appealing to emotion can also be a very effective way to mislead people.

As this case has attracted so much attention, let's look at it in more detail. If you listen to the audio on that video, you will hear that they thought the object was a "worm of some kind". Only later, after the video was made, did they claim it was a plastic straw. The object was brown and 15cm long, which is far shorter than a plastic straw. I checked to see how they knew it was a plastic straw. It turns out they never analysed the object as any professional scientist would do. So, they had zero proof it was made of plastic! Think about that for a moment—a huge movement sweeping the world based on a video containing not one iota of scientific evidence. I don't think we should be banning plastic straws all around the world based on one unsubstantiated YouTube video. Do you? If you want to see their feeble, non-scientific account of the turtle incident, here is the reference.

N. J. Robinson & C. Figgener, Marine Turtle Newsletter 147, 2015

I was wondering whether it is common for animals to get things stuck up their noses, so I did a search on YouTube and found two videos right away. In both cases, a dog had been playing in the forest and got a stick stuck up its nose. The videos were identical to the famous turtle case. The dogs sneezed and the object was slowly removed. I was wondering why environmentalists hadn't called for a ban on sticks, trees, and forests after the two dog videos. When they find an alleged piece of plastic up a turtle's nose, they want to ban plastics. So, why not ban sticks because they are just as much threat to dog health? It makes you think, doesn't it?

Stick Removed From Dog's Nostril - https://youtu.be/C0AHXSf2IJQ
A 5-inch stick was removed from this dog's nose - https://youtu.be/jGx2cD9lsz4

It seems that environmentalists are determined to demonize plastics whether or not they have evidence and whether or not their arguments make sense. It is up to us to resist these rather transparent attempts at deception.

Let's get some perspective by looking at the amount of straws in the ocean. The data shows that 0.6% of plastic in the ocean comes from the US, of which 0.02% are straws. So, eliminating straws from the US would reduce ocean plastic by 0.00012%. Why do the environmental groups have such an obsession with a product that makes virtually zero difference? Why not focus on something that actually matters instead?

One could argue that the 0.6% figure for ocean plastic coming from the US is actually higher, in part because of all the waste exported to Asia. That's a fair point. However, the export of such waste has been outlawed now. The fact remains that we need to focus our efforts in the geographical regions where the greatest problems exist.

PLASTIC LITTER IN RIVERS

Litter in rivers has been studied very extensively, so we know a lot about it. The first point to note is that although plastic is all we hear about in the media, it is certainly not the only type of material found in rivers.

Looking at the plastic portion of the river litter only, we find a breakdown of the items. One might expect straws and bags to dominate, but they only represent one per cent each of the items found. Again, why is all the attention from environmental groups on an item that hardly registers in the data? Surely, if we want to make an impact, we should be investing our time and money on the main culprits such as cigarette buts and packaging. I would seem that the goal of the so-called environmental groups is not to clean up the environment. Perhaps they are more concerned with being popular and keeping the donations rolling in. That would explain why they don't dare rile up the public by putting the spotlight on smokers. Maybe they feel it's safer for them to distract us with meaningless items like straws. That way people can feel like they are making a difference and the flow of donations can go on unimpeded. That's the only explanation I can think of for their obsession with items that don't matter.

Rank	Plastic Category	Amount Found
1	Plastic Bottles	14%
2	Food Wrappers	12%
3	Cigarette Butts	9%
4	Takeaway Food Containers	6%
5	Cotton Bud Sticks	5%
6	Cups	4%
7	Sanitary Items	3%
8	Smoking- Related Packaging	2%
9	Straws, Stirrers, Cutlery	1%
10	Plastic Bags	1%

From the Plastic Rivers Report - Earthwatch.org.uk

We also need to consider where this river plastic originates. It turns out that the vast majority comes from 10 rivers in Asia and Africa. Why then are the green groups targeting the US and Europe when there is less of a problem in those regions? Perhaps it's because that's where the money is. If we are to address this problem, then we have to take action in the right place. Perhaps green GMOs should use some of their massive income to install facilities to remove plastic from those 10 rivers. That is what they would do if they truly wanted to make a difference.

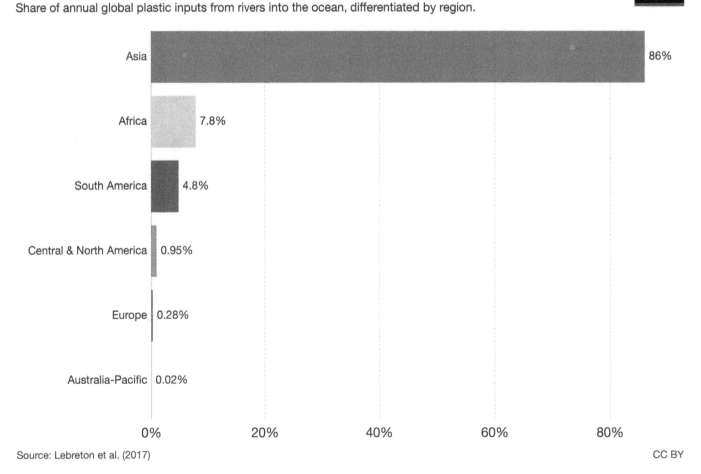

Global river plastic input to the ocean by region, 2015

Share of annual global plastic inputs from rivers into the ocean, differentiated by region.

Our World in Data

Region	
Asia	86%
Africa	7.8%
South America	4.8%
Central & North America	0.95%
Europe	0.28%
Australia-Pacific	0.02%

0%   20%   40%   60%   80%

Source: Lebreton et al. (2017)

Plastic entering the oceans comes from Asia and Africa

Why then are we banning plastics in regions like the US and Europe?

PLASTICS LITTER ON BEACHES

Litter on beaches attracts a lot of attention, in large part because it is so visible. People see it on their holidays, and the problem is especially severe in some popular vacation locations in Asia. We have high profile stars drawing attention to the issue. This can be a good thing, but only if the stars give us correct advice.

F1 world champion Lewis Hamilton cleans up plastic littered beach

The reigning Formula One world champion called the litter "disgusting" and urged the public not to buy plastic or polystyrene.

F1 world champion Lewis Hamilton cleans up plastic littered beach, Russel Hope, Sky News, August 8th 2018

It is admirable that stars feel the need to get involved and help. What amazes me, though, is that they feel qualified to advise us on a topic which they know virtually nothing about. It would be like me giving Lewis Hamilton advice on his racing technique. I know that would be inappropriate and unhelpful, so I don't do it. Ideally, our stars would be wise enough to leave plastics advice to plastics experts. Lewis's advice is to "not buy plastic or polystyrene", but is that the best advice?

Let's check the facts so we can correctly identify the problem and the appropriate solution. Where does beach litter come from? Well, fortunately, the topic has been studied for decades, so there is good data to draw from. From these studies, we know that the type of litter is very different depending on the type of beach.

A. M. Addamo, P. Laroche, G. Hanke, Top Marine Beach Litter Items in Europe A review and synthesis based on beach litter data, Joint Research Centre Technical Reports, European Union 2017

TOURIST BEACH LITTER

It is interesting to read articles about beach litter in different countries and locations. A study in Brazil collected about 13,000 pieces of litter from 100 meter-long strips across nine beaches. They showed that cigarette butts were dominant along with plastics, food scraps, and wooden skewers. Cigarette butts comprise a cellulose acetate (a type of naturally-derived plastic) filter and a paper wrapper.

"The most-represented items of anthropogenic litter in the evaluated samples were plastic, food scraps, and wood (wooden skewers). With respect to items composed of plastic, the majority were cigarette butts (45%). Additionally, cigarette butts made up 26% of all anthropogenic litter samples collected."

M. C. B. Araújo, J. S. Silva-Cavalcanti and M. F. Costa, Anthropogenic Litter on Beaches With Different Levels of Development and Use: A Snapshot of a Coast in Pernambuco (Brazil), Frontiers in Marine Science, 5 (233), 2018

The authors also noted:

"The beaches with lower levels of urbanization also had smaller quantities of anthropogenic litter. Items related to beach users were predominant for most of the beaches. The confirmation that beach users are primarily responsible for the generation of anthropogenic litter may contribute to the development of strategies to reduce the problem, such as installing bins and distribution containers for anthropogenic litter collection and designing educational campaigns for beach users."

As we see, the litter on a beach is caused mainly by the people on the beach. This is an important point. The public and the stars alike go to tourist beaches and assume that the litter they see there is representative of litter on all beaches, but that's not the case. As the authors correctly state, the people on the beach caused the litter there, so education and other methods to alter human behaviour are recommended to solve the problem.

Another article noted tourism is an important source of income for beach locations, but that people avoid highly littered beaches. The irony is that it is tourists who created the litter in the first place. This creates a self-spreading effect whereby people litter one beach until it is no longer pretty and then they simply go find other, pristine beaches they can ruin.

"In coastal California, visitors are reported to travel longer distances to avoid beaches with more waste and in Brazil, a recent survey reports that 85% of beachgoers will avoid beaches with high litter loads (>15 pieces per m²). This is also interesting in light of numerous reports (and anecdotal evidence) that beachgoers themselves can be a contributing source of debris."

J . Vince & B. D. Harvesty, Governance Solutions to the Tragedy of the Commons That Marine Plastics Have Become, Frontiers in Marine Science, 5 (214), 2018

"Changing individual behavior is key to preventing litter."

We all need to look in the mirror if we want to stop litter

REMOTE BEACH LITTER

At first, it was assumed that all beaches contained the same types of litter. People would visit a tourist beach and assume the litter there was typical. But as we just learned, the type of litter found on a beach accessible to people is actually caused by those people. Most beaches are not frequented by tourists, which means that most people have no idea what's on those beaches. Scientists do, though, because they have studied them.

As long ago as 1972, the inimitable Professor Gerald Scott published the first findings on the topic. He found that isolated beaches were dominated by fishing nets and ropes rather than the litter found on beaches frequented by people. Professor Scott was a leading authority on polymer degradation, and he noted at the time that items made of high-density polyethylene and polypropylene degraded rather rapidly when exposed to the elements.

G. Scott, Plastics packaging and coastal pollution, International Journal of Environmental Studies, 3 (1-4), pp 35-36 1972

Occasionally, a remote beach will contain a large proportion of litter other than the normal nets and fishing gear. In such instances, it is normally claimed that the items must have drifted there on ocean currents. However, a recent study debunked that idea. Scientists studied the litter on the beach of a remote uninhabited island in the South Atlantic Gyre over a period of decades. They found that in the 1980s some items did indeed drift 3,000 miles from land. However, in recent times, the litter was too new to have drifted from land. They could tell the age of the litter because of manufacturing codes on the bottles and other items. Another clue was that PET bottles were crushed with the caps on, which is what sailors do to preserve space on ships. They concluded that most of the litter on the remote island came from Chinese shipping vessels that had dumped it overboard:

"Currently, 75% of bottles are from Asia, with most from China. The recent manufacture dates indicate that few bottles could have drifted from Asia, and presumably are dumped from ships, in contravention of International Convention for the Prevention of Pollution from Ships regulations. Our results question the widely held assumption that most plastic debris at sea comes from land-based sources."

P. G. Ryan et al., Rapid increase in Asian bottles in the South Atlantic Ocean indicates major debris inputs from ships, PNAS Latest Articles www.pnas.org/cgi/doi/10.1073/pnas.1909816116

Once again, we find that the litter is not magically "making its way onto the beaches" but is being dumped into the ocean on purpose by law-breaking individuals. The researchers also noted that the litter was degrading rather rapidly, contrary to what we are always told. A later chapter deals with polymer degradation in detail.

In an interview for the Associated Press:

"Everyone talks about saving the oceans by stopping using plastic bags, straws and single use packaging. That's important, but when we head out on the ocean, that's not necessarily what we find."

Ocean plastic waste probably comes from ships, report says, Ivan Couronne, Associated Press, September 30th 2019

BEACH LITTER TRENDS

The OSPAR reports are very detailed, spanning several countries and many years. They conclude that beach litter is decreasing significantly for all the beaches studied. Nets were the most common type of litter, and polystyrene pieces were the second most common.

"Data of 2010-2015 show decreasing significant trends for litter items found on the monitoring beaches during this six year period."

It appears that we are making good progress. Although more work remains to be done, the situation is not as hopeless as we are led to believe. Certain environmental groups want us to believe that the problem is urgent and worsening at an alarming rate. This is a compelling story, but it just isn't true.

Environmental groups are hyping up the dangers of single-use bags and straws when these items are not the problem. Cigarettes are the number one littered item worldwide, but we hear no mention of them in the press. It was also shown that between 2009 and 2013, litter from plastic bottles and bags decreased significantly, while litter from cigarette butts doubled.

G. Hanke, Marine Beach Litter in Europe – Top Items, JRC Technical Reports, JRC103929, European Commission, 2016

An article looked in detail at the problem of beach litter and suggested several ways to monitor it as well as a multi-faceted approach to solving the problem:

1. Prevention of waste and litter
2. Mitigation (i.e., recycling and design for recycle)
3. Education through beach clean-ups and advertising
4. Political will and government action to build waste handling capacity

A. T. Williams & N. Rangel-Buitrago, Marine Litter: Solutions for a Major Environmental Problem, Journal of Coastal Research, 35 (3), pp 648-663 2019

REGIONAL DIFFERENCES

If we look at a global map, we see that the developed world generates the majority of waste. That should come as no surprise.

Plastic waste generation, 2010

Total plastic waste generation by country, measured in tonnes per year. This measures total plastic waste generation prior to management and therefore does not represent the quantity of plastic at risk of polluting waterways, rivers and the ocean environment. High-income countries typically have well-managed waste streams and therefore low levels of plastic pollution to external environments.

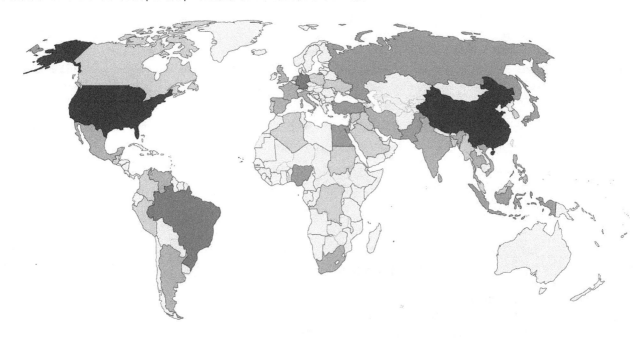

0 tonnes   2.5 million tonnes   10 million tonnes   >50 million tonnes
No data   1 million tonnes   5 million tonnes   25 million tonnes

Source: OWID based on Jambeck et al. (2015) & World Bank

Looking at that map, one would think that those countries shaded with darker colours, need to clean up their act as they are causing an environmental crisis. That is certainly what the environmental groups tell us. They ask for donations in Europe and the USA to help clean up the mess. However, that map does not tell the whole story. Now consider this next map, which shows the mismanaged waste instead of the generation of waste.

Share of plastic waste that is inadequately managed, 2010

Inadequately disposed waste is not formally managed and includes disposal in dumps or open, uncontrolled landfills, where it is not fully contained. Inadequately managed waste has high risk of polluting rivers and oceans.

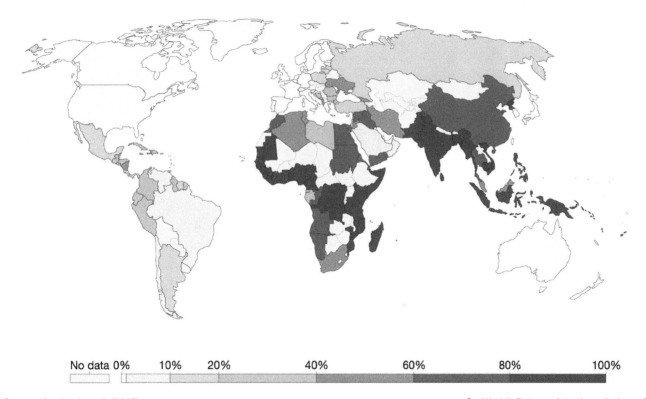

No data 0%   10%   20%   40%   60%   80%   100%

Source: Jambeck et al. (2015)   OurWorldInData.org/plastic-pollution · CC BY
Note: This does not include 'littered' plastic waste, which is approximately 2% of total waste.

This tells a very different story. We see that although the USA and Europe create a lot of waste, they manage it effectively. In contrast, other countries generate far less waste but are extremely ineffective at managing the waste, so it escapes into the environment. As those countries catch up in management technology and policy, we can expect to see a radical reduction in waste entering our rivers and oceans.

CONCLUSIONS

Litter has been studied in detail. We know with certainty that litter is caused by human behaviour and not by inanimate objects, whether they be made of paper, plastic, metal, or glass. Once we know the true cause of the litter, we can take effective action to correct the problem. Ocean litter is largely due to the fishing industry abandoning nets and ropes that cause harm to marine wildlife. On the other hand, tourist beach and land litter is caused by irresponsible humans.

Consider this analogy. When my children drop stuff on the floor of their room, I ask them to pick it up. They put it there, so it's their responsibility to pick it up. The rule is so obvious that it applies across cultures and countries all around the world. Now let's imagine a different way to handle the same situation. Let us suppose that my kids have dropped a pair of blue jeans on their bedroom floor, and I call Levi Strauss and Co. and ask them to pick them up because they made the jeans, so they are therefore somehow responsible. If I really did call Levi's, my wife would ask a psychiatrist to check my sanity, and rightly so. Asking the manufacturer to clean up our mess is such an obviously stupid approach that most people would laugh out loud at it.

Now let us look at litter. Every day we see pictures of beaches or parks strewn with wrappers and other junk dropped there by people. Then we hear calls for Coca-Cola to pick up the cans and bottles and for Nestlé to pick up the candy wrappers or for the plastics industry to clean up all the plastic. As we just pointed out, it's the person who dropped the litter who is responsible for cleaning it up, not the manufacturer. It is the government's job to use taxes collected from the sale of the soda can or candy bar to clean up any litter. That's one of the reasons we pay taxes. In many countries, this system actually works really well.

As you may know, the pressure from the public became so intense that the plastics industry committed $1.5BN to clean up the oceans. They have volunteered to clean up a mess that's not theirs. Guess what the response to this is? I see people attacking them online and asking why they don't do more. It makes no sense to blame the manufacturers because people cause litter, and to solve that, we need to change human behaviour.

If it were up to me, every litterer would have to clean up a thousand pieces of litter for every one they drop. Imagine if there was a $1,000 fine plus a month of community service whereby the litterer had to clean the streets in his or her own neighbourhood. Imagine the shame of it. Image the added effectiveness if repeat offenders were given a criminal record. The litter problem would be solved in no time at all.

Lie #3 – Plastics are responsible for litter.

Truth – Whether the litter is paper, metal, glass or plastic, the cause is human behaviour and the solution is to change that behaviour through education and regulation.

CHAPTER FOUR
MICROPLASTICS

MICROPLASTICS

Oceans are tremendously important to our ecosystem. They cover about two-thirds of our planet and extend to tremendous depths. In terms of size and diversity of life, they are something to marvel at—and certainly something worth protecting. We have all heard the stories of microplastics in the ocean and the negative effects associated with them, so this is a topic worth looking into.

MICROPLASTICS

A lot has been written about microplastics. So, what are they? What are they made of? How do they get into the ocean? And, most importantly, are they toxic? Some articles say that we're not sure whether they are harmful, and there are others claiming that they leach toxins into the ocean.

"Microplastics are defined as plastic pieces that are between one micrometer (one millionth of a meter) and five millimeters in size. Nanoplastics are even smaller than one micrometer."

Microplastics are estimated to make up 8% by weight of all plastics in the oceans, which is a substantial amount and well worth a closer look.

L. Lebreton et al., Evidence that the Great Pacific Garbage Patch is rapidly accumulating plastic, Scientific Reports, 8:4666, 2018

WHERE DO MICROPLASTICS COME FROM?

By investigating the sources of microplastics, we can design strategies to deal with them. For example, 35% comes from synthetic fibres that come from washing synthetic fabrics. The solution to this issue is water filtration, and we know that works because water purification facilities already filter out microplastics from drinking water. Almost 30% comes from car tires, which is harder to deal with. Replacing rubber with another material is unlikely because it performs so much better than the alternatives. A switch to greater use of trains for transportation would have an effect, and it may even be possible to program cars to accelerate and decelerate smoothly to avoid excessive abrasion and wear.

Global Releases of Primary Microplastics to the Worlds Oceans

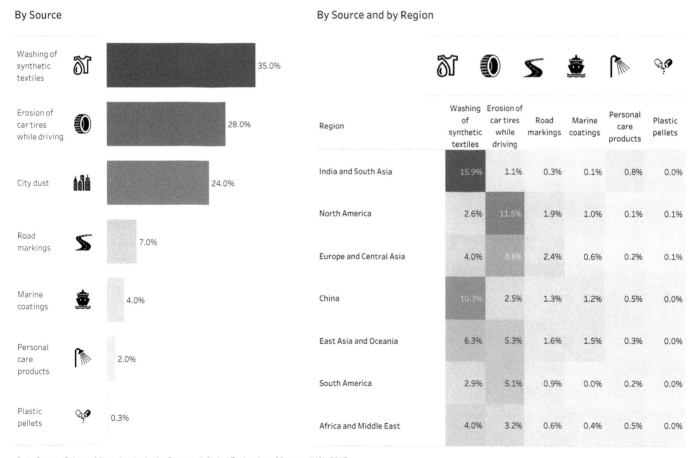

By Source

Source	Value
Washing of synthetic textiles	35.0%
Erosion of car tires while driving	28.0%
City dust	24.0%
Road markings	7.0%
Marine coatings	4.0%
Personal care products	2.0%
Plastic pellets	0.3%

By Source and by Region

Region	Washing of synthetic textiles	Erosion of car tires while driving	Road markings	Marine coatings	Personal care products	Plastic pellets
India and South Asia	15.9%	1.1%	0.3%	0.1%	0.8%	0.0%
North America	2.6%	11.5%	1.9%	1.0%	0.1%	0.1%
Europe and Central Asia	4.0%	8.6%	2.4%	0.6%	0.2%	0.1%
China	10.3%	2.5%	1.3%	1.2%	0.5%	0.0%
East Asia and Oceania	6.3%	5.3%	1.6%	1.5%	0.3%	0.0%
South America	2.9%	5.1%	0.9%	0.0%	0.2%	0.0%
Africa and Middle East	4.0%	3.2%	0.6%	0.4%	0.5%	0.0%

Data Source: Primary Microplastics in the Oceans - A Global Evaluation of Sources IUCN 2017

For some reason, many articles talk about plastic pellets as though they are a major problem. But according to the data above, they account for only 0.3% of plastic in the ocean, and regulations have already halved their amount since the 1980s. Personal care products, such as the microbeads used as exfoliants in facial scrubs, have become a target as well. They account for just 2% of plastics in the ocean, are made of safe polyethylene, and have already been removed in many cases. Clearly, microbeads should not be in the oceans, but there is an overblown emphasis on them while the major culprits are entirely overlooked in the press.

Plastic pellets are declining in amount due to increased attention and regulation:

"Long-term studies on seabirds have shown that measures to reduce loss of plastics to the environment do have relatively rapid effects. After considerable attention to the massive loss of industrial pellets to the marine environment in the early 1980s, improvements in production and transport methods were reflected in a visible result in the marine environment within one to two decades: several studies from around the globe showed that by the early 2000s the number of industrial granules in seabird stomachs had approximately halved from levels observed in the 1980s...These examples indicate that it is possible to reduce deleterious impacts from marine plastic debris on marine wild- life in shorter time frames than the longevity of the material might suggest."

Chapter 4 in Marine Anthropogenic Litter, M. Bergmann, L. Gutow, M. Klages (Eds.)
Springer, Berlin, 2015

It is good news that plastics pellets were significantly reduced in such a short timeframe, as it shows how quickly progress can be made once a problem is identified.

Although the pellets (which environmentalists often refer to as "nurdles") and exfoliant beads should not be in our oceans, should we not focus most of our attention on items that actually make a difference, like the 35% from washing clothes, the 28% from car tire wear, and the 24% from city dust?

"The results show that laundering 6 kg of synthetic materials could release between 137,951–728,789 fibres per wash"

I. E. Napper, R. C. Thompson, Release of synthetic microplastic plastic fibres from domestic washing machines: Effects of fabric type and washing conditions, Marine Pollution Bulletin, 112, (1–2), Pages 39-45, 15 November 2016

WHAT KIND OF PLASTIC IS IT?

People have collected samples from the ocean and analysed them using standard chemical tools to identify them. The microplastic particles are predominantly polyethylene and polypropylene, which should come as no surprise because together these two plastics make up over 50% of all thermoplastics sold.

Market share of commodity plastics
R. Geyer, J. R. Jambeck & K. L. Law, Production, use, and fate of all plastics ever made, Science Advances, 3e1700782, 2017

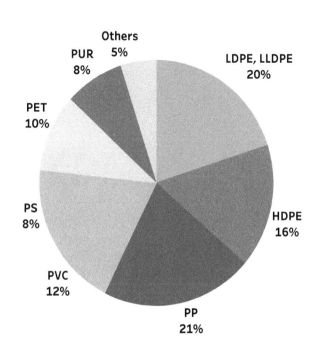

- Others 5%
- PUR 8%
- LDPE, LLDPE 20%
- PET 10%
- HDPE 16%
- PS 8%
- PP 21%
- PVC 12%

A study from Italy found the most predominant microplastics under 1mm in size to be PE (48%) and PP (34%). So, 82% was either PE or PP.

A. Vianello et al., Microplastic particles in sediments of Lagoon of Venice, Italy: First observations on occurrence, spatial patterns and identification, Estuarine, Coastal and Shelf Science, 130 (20), Pages 54-61 2013

Another study said, "Plastic was detected in 49 out of 64 fish (77%), with 2.3 pieces on average and up to 15 pieces per individual" and "most were polyethylene (52.0%) or polypropylene (43.3%)". So, in this case, over 93% of the microplastic was either PE or PP.

K. Tanaka, H. Takada, Microplastic fragments and microbeads in digestive tracts of planktivorous fish from urban coastal waters, Scientific Reports 6, 34351 2016

The same study goes on to say, "Eighty per cent of the plastics ranged in size from 150μm to 1000μm," meaning that the particles are between about 0.1mm and 1mm in size.

A detailed study was also done on the types of plastic, their concentrations, and how they vary in the water (at the waterfront and in the beach sand).

N. Scott et al., Particle characteristics of microplastics contaminating the mussel Mytilus edulis and their surrounding environments, Marine Pollution Bulletin, 146, pp 125-133 2019

So, we know that PE and PP are the main constituents of microplastics.

MICROPLASTICS AND TOXICITY

Microplastics do not belong in the ocean. In fact, no waste, litter or pollution belongs there. However, given that it is there, let's look at the science and see what we know about the potential problems. In this book, we have debunked several common myths, and microplastics is one area where there are several scientific articles claiming to show toxic effects.

Microbeads are leaching toxic chemicals into fish, sparking public health fears

Esther Han, The Sydney Morning Herald, August 16th 2016

The above headline referred to work done on microbeads from personal care products. The article states that microbeads can transfer toxic substances to fish and then, potentially, on to people who eat the fish.

Here is an overview of some articles that raise serious concerns about microplastics as determined by exposing laboratory fish and oysters to microplastics.

Article 1 – Fish and microbeads
This article expresses concern that these particles concentrate toxins, which could eventually affect humans.

P. Wardrop, Chemical Pollutants Sorbed to Ingested Microbeads from Personal Care Products Accumulate in Fish, Environ. Sci. Technol., 50, 4037–4044 2016

Article 2 - Oyster reproduction
According to this study, polystyrene particles have serious effects on oysters.

Sussarellu et al., Oyster reproduction is affected by exposure to polystyrene microplastics, PNAS March 1, 113 (9) 2430-2435 2016

Article 3 – Bass
These workers find that microplastics affect fish by concentrating mercury, a heavy metal.

L. G. A. Barboza et al., Microplastics cause neurotoxicity, oxidative damage and energy-related changes and interact with the bioaccumulation of mercury in the European seabass, Dicentrarchus labrax (Linnaeus, 1758), Aquatic Toxicology 195, 49–57, 2018

Article 4 – Zebrafish
They claimed that polystyrene microparticles accumulate in fish gills, livers, and gut.

Y. Lu, Uptake and Accumulation of Polystyrene Microplastics in Zebrafish (Danio rerio) and Toxic Effects in Liver, Environ. Sci. Technol., Apr 5;50(7):4054-60 2016

Article 5 – Fish and nanoparticles
These workers stated, "polystyrene nanoparticles have severe effects on both behaviour and on metabolism in fish".

K. Mattsson et al., Altered behavior, physiology, and metabolism in fish exposed to polystyrene nanoparticles, Environmental Science and Technology 49(1), 2014

There are several other articles like these. The implications are frightening, so I read each of these articles carefully along with all the others I could find. What I found was that these articles are all junk science. That's a bold claim, so let me explain what I mean by that. One cannot simply dismiss studies without very good reasons. In short, these articles violated the basic rules of science. Let us consider each rule violation in turn.

1. Studies used 100 to 10 million times too much microplastic

They used vastly more microplastic than is actually in the ocean. By using unrealistic concentrations, you get unrealistic results. For example, if you eat an apple a day, apples are safe. If you eat a million per day, they are not.

2. Studies used the wrong kind of plastic

The vast majority of studies were done using a kind of microplastic that does not exist in the ocean. They purchased cross-linked polystyrene particles for their studies because that was convenient for them. As the microplastics in the ocean are predominantly PE and PP, so studies should be conducted on PE and PP.

3. The used the wrong size of particle

Many studies used nanoparticles instead of microplastics. Nanoparticles have a lot more surface area than the microparticles we find in the ocean.

4. They failed to do control experiments

Proper experiments include controls. For example, half the fish should be fed microplastics and the other half should be fed another kind of particles for example soil or sand. This tells us whether microplastics are harmful compared to other particles the fish are normally exposed to. These controls were not done.

5. They designed experiments to show toxic effects that are not actually present

In some studies, they pre-soaked microplastics in toxic chemicals and then exposed the fish to the poison-soaked plastic. They concluded that plastics release toxins and poison fish. This is method is unrealistic and deceitful.

6. They starved the fish

Some studies replaced 10% of the fish's food with microplastics and then reported mild health effects. Firstly, that is far too much microplastic to use. Also, we know that reducing the calories an animal receives can alter its health.

7. They falsified their results

One group was reported for falsifying their results. An investigation was performed, and they were found guilty, so the publication was retracted. This is very rare in science, and it shows you just how far people will go to make microplastics look bad.

The article they reported was:

O. M. Lönnstedt and P. Eklöv, Environmentally relevant concentrations of microplastic particles influence larval fish ecology. Science 352: 1213-1216, 2016

As a reviewer for scientific journals, I would have rejected every one of these articles and blocked their publication. If I had funded their research, I would have demanded a refund. This is shamefully poor junk science, but it makes headline news because it purports to show dangers, albeit fictional ones.

It is not just my opinion that the work was poorly done. Lenz and Nielsen found that out of ten studies on microplastics, all showed actual microplastic concentrations in the range $1 ngL^{-1}$ and $1 \mu gL^{-1}$. Then they looked at the concentration used when checking for possible toxic effects and noted that toxicity studies were all done using 100 to 10 million times more microplastic than we actually find in the ocean. That's bad science. They actually called out those other scientists for using such unrealistically high concentrations and implored them to do better in future. As a scientist myself, I have never in my career seen another instance where studies were done so poorly that fellow scientists felt the need to point it out and demand better. It is impossible to know why the studies were done so poorly, but it is easier to get funding when your results are dramatic, even if they are not realistic.

Lenz, R., Enders, K., & Nielsen, T. G. 2016. Microplastic exposure studies should be environmentally realistic. Proceedings of the National Academy of Sciences, 113(29), E4121 - E4122

Here is a published comment on the zebrafish article just mentioned.

> "Unfortunately, inaccurate and poorly presented histopathological data are recurrent themes in ecotoxicological publications. Such deficiencies are particularly egregious in the present case, as the study conclusions depend heavily on the histopathologic results which will now persist in the literature and potentially spawn further misguided research."

L. Baumann et al., Comment on "Uptake and Accumulation of Polystyrene Microplastics in zebrafish (Danio rerio) and Toxic Effects in Liver", Environ. Sci. Technol., 50, 22, 12521-12522, 2016

These researchers point out that the zebrafish work was unprofessional and misleading. Again, it is rare in science that one group's work is so poor that other scientists feel compelled to correct them.

HOW SAFE ARE PE AND PP?

Toxicity of plastic is a complex topic, but for the purposes of this article, let's keep it simple. Is the type of microplastic found in the ocean safe? As we know, those plastics are predominantly PE and PP. The answer should be obvious to most people because we store our food in polyethylene bags (Ziploc® is one well-known brand) and polypropylene boxes (Tupperware®, for example). We have done so for several decades. The plastic used is food-contact approved and tested very thoroughly to make sure that there are no harmful additives. Those plastics contain extremely low levels of additives anyway, typically well under 0.1% by weight. As shown in the table, there are barely any additives in polyolefins and all of them are FDA approved for indirect food contact. So, we can be assured that the plastics have an excellent safety record.

Ingredient	Function	Concentration (%)
PE or PP	Plastic material	99.96
Calcium stearate	Acid scavenger	0.02
Phosphite	Processing stabilizer	0.01
Hindered phenol	In-use stabilizer	0.02

Typical formulation for polyethylene or polypropylene

OTHER PLASTICS AND ADDITIVES

Expanded polystyrene was tested to see if any toxic substances were leached into food (e.g., hot soup) and whether the leachate was toxic. The first set of experiments showed no detectable compounds, so they repeated the experiments with a more sensitive instrument. They did finally detect ethyl benzene under extreme and unrealistic conditions. Even then they found 100x lower concentrations than the WHO's safety limit. This was under heating to 95°C for up to 30 minutes. In other words, they tried as hard as they could, even resorting to totally unrealistic conditions and still could not come close to finding a problem. They concluded:

C. Thaysen et al., Leachate From Expanded Polystyrene Cups Is Toxic to Aquatic Invertebrates (Ceriodaphnia dubia), Front. Mar. Sci. 5:71. 2018

This matches other studies showing that leaching of styrene from polystyrene is very low and unrealistic conditions must be used to get higher values.

Polystyrene cups and containers: Styrene migration, M. S. Tawfik, A. Huyghebaert, Polystyrene cups and containers: Styrene migration', Food Additives & Contaminants: Part A, 15: 5, 592-599 1998

A detailed study found that while PE, PP and PET contain only very low levels of toxic chemicals, two significant thermoplastics that can contain larger amounts of extractible small-molecule additives are polyurethane and PVC. Furthermore, they discovered that PLA, a so-called green, degradable plastic was among the worst materials tested.

L. Zimmermann et al., Benchmarking the in Vitro Toxicity and Chemical Composition of Plastic Consumer Products, Environ. Sci. Technol., 53, 19, 11467-11477 2019

Speaking of PVC, for decades, phthalate plasticizers were scrutinized, and eventually some were banned. Lead stabilizers used to be popular in PVC but have since been replaced by safe alternatives.

Brominated flame retardants were added to some plastics to save lives. In fact, regulations required that they be added to furniture foam and electrical housings to prevent deaths by fire and toxic smoke. In later years, some of them were regulated out and replaced by safer alternatives.

All of these changes are invisible to the public, but the plastics industry is continually testing and developing better, safer products. Some companies, like P&G, take caution to the next level and specify that all the additives in their plastic products are food contact approved. This included shampoo bottles and other items that are never actually in contact with food.

PERSPECTIVE

Let's take a step back and think about this safety topic for a moment. If using plastics really did present a significant danger, we would know by now because we would all be sick or dead. It's the same with the much talked about potential danger from cell phones. Scientists have done huge studies for decades and still cannot show any significant effect at all. There is no reason to panic about plastic safety; besides, there are strict regulations that get tighter all the time, so when new evidence comes in, action is taken.

As an example, when I worked at BASF, a customer demanded vanishingly low limits for formaldehyde in plastic. Just because new analytical equipment can now detect molecules down to parts per million or even parts per billion levels does not mean there is a problem. Furthermore, people often look at the results out of context. What do I mean by that? Well, the customer's demands for the formaldehyde in the plastic was way less than the formaldehyde you would get from biting into an apple or taking a walk in the forest. Do you see what I mean? Their demand for "safety" was way over the top. We need perspective, not knee-jerk reactions.

Even the food we eat contains known toxins. Red meat causes cancer, so do alcoholic drinks and even hot drinks. Just because something is natural does not mean it is safe or green. Conversely, synthetic products are not necessarily harmful. As we have seen, they are often safer and greener than the natural alternative. An ingredients list for a 100% natural cabbage contains multiple cancer-causing chemicals, which are manufactured by the cabbage itself.

CONTAINS: GLUCOSINOLATES (2-PROPENYL GLUCOSINOLATE (SINIGRIN), 3-METHYLTHIOPROPYL GLUCOSINOLATE, 3-METHYLSULFINYLPROPYL GLUCOSINOLATE, 3-BUTENYL GLUCOSINOLATE, 2-HYDROXY-3-BUTENYL GLUCOSINOLATE, 4-METHYLTHIOBUTYL GLUCOSINOLATE, 4-METHYLSULFINYLBUTYL GLUCOSINOLATE, 4-METHYLSULFONYLBUTYL GLUCOSINOLATE, BENZYL GLUCOSINOLATE, 2-PHENYLETHYL GLUCOSINOLATE, PROPYL GLUCOSINOLATE, BUTYL GLUCOSINOLATE); **INDOLE GLUCOSINOLATES AND RELATED INDOLES:** 3-INDOLYLMETHYL GLUCOSINOLATE (GLUCOBRASSICIN), 1-METHOXY-3-INDOLYLMETHYL GLUCOSINOLATE (NEOGLUCOBRASSICIN), INDOLE-3-CARBINOL, INDOLE-3-ACETONITRILE, BIS(3-INDOLYL)METHANE); **ISOTHIOCYANATES AND GOITRIN:** (ALLYL ISOTHIOCYANATE, 3-METHYLTHIOPROPYL ISOTHIOCYANATE, 3-METHYLSULFINYLPROPYL ISOTHIOCYANATE, 3-BUTENYL ISOTHIOCYANATE, 5-VINYLOXAZOLIDINE-2-THIONE (GOITRIN), 4-METHYLTHIOBUTYL ISOTHIOCYANATE, 4-METHYLSULFINYLBUTYL ISOTHIOCYANATE, 4-METHYLSULFONYLBUTYL ISOTHIOCYANATE, 4-PENTENYL ISOTHIOCYANATE, BENZYL ISOTHIOCYANATE, PHENYLETHYL ISOTHIOCYANATE); **CYANIDES:** 1-CYANO-2,3-EPITHIOPROPANE, 1-CYANO-3,4-EPITHIOBUTANE, 1-CYANO-3,4-EPITHIOPENTANE, THREO-1-CYANO-2-HYDROXY-3,4-EPITHIOBUTANE, ERYTHRO-1-CYANO-2-HYDROXY-3,4-EPITHIOBUTANE, 2-PHENYLPROPIONITRILE, ALLYL CYANIDE, 1-CYANO-2-HYDROXY-3-BUTENE, 1-CYANO-3-METHYLSULFINYLPROPANE, 1-CYANO-4-METHYLSULFINYLBUTANE); TERPENES: MENTHOL, NEOMENTHOL, ISOMENTHOL, CARVONE **PHENOLS:** (2-METHOXYPHENOL, 3-CAFFOYLQUINIC ACID (CHLOROGENIC ACID), 4-CAFFOYLQUINIC) 4-CAFFOYLQUINIC ACID, 5-CAFFOYLQUINIC ACID (NEOCHLOROGENIC ACID), 4-(P-COUMAROYL)QUINIC ACID, 5-(P-COUMAROYL)QUINIC ACID, 5-FERULOYLQUINIC ACID)

RED = CARCINOGENIC
ORANGE = MUTAGENIC/CLASTOGENIC

Natural toxic compounds in cabbage - with permission from James Kennedy

When we take a moment to check the latest statistics, we find that cancer mortality is lower than ever, so there is no cause for panic.

"The cancer death rate rose until 1991, then fell continuously through 2017, resulting in an overall decline of 29% that translates into an estimated 2.9 million fewer cancer deaths than would have occurred if peak rates had persisted. This progress is driven by long-term declines in death rates for the four leading cancers (lung, colorectal, breast, prostate); however, over the past decade (2008-2017), reductions slowed for female breast and colorectal cancers, and halted for prostate cancer. In contrast, declines accelerated for lung cancer, from 3% annually during 2008 through 2013 to 5% during 2013 through 2017 in men and from 2% to almost 4% in women, spurring the largest ever single-year drop in overall cancer mortality of 2.2% from 2016 to 2017. Yet lung cancer still caused more deaths in 2017 than breast, prostate, colorectal, and brain cancers combined."

R . L. Siegel et al., Cancer statistics, 2020, American Cancer Society, Ca Cancer J. Clin. 70:7–30 2020

The main four causes are lung, colorectal, breast, and prostate, with lung alone accounting for more than the next three combined. In an earlier chapter, we saw that cigarettes are a main cause of litter and now we see that they are a leading cause of health problems too. If you are worried about your health, then don't smoke, don't get sunburnt, and eat a healthy diet with plenty of fresh fruit and vegetables.

While we are on the subject of toxic substances, here is a noteworthy piece of information I came across while researching for this book:

"Statements from the MoD also reveal that between 1945 and 1957 it scuttled 24 ships packed with 137 000 tons of chemical weapons at two sites in the Atlantic. One is 1600 kilometres southwest of Land's End, around Hurds Deep, but the other is a large area beginning 100 kilometres northwest of Northern Ireland and southeast of Rockall Deep. Eight of the ships are sitting at depths of less than 2000 metres, and the shallowest is in 500 metres of water. Both sites are also home to thousands of tons of radioactive waste from Britain's nuclear programme."

Rob Edwards, Danger from the deep, New Scientist, 18th November 1995

It is amazing to think that hundreds of thousands of tons of chemical weapons have been sunk intentionally and yet we hear virtually nothing about this. We have people worrying about trace additives in plastics when there are far larger problems, that truly deserve attention.

The article went on to say:

"Late last month, the armed forces minister Nicholas Soames told parliament that the material dumped in the Atlantic includes 17 000 tons of captured German bombs filled with the nerve gas tabun. The scientists at the Marine Laboratory in Aberdeen say that another nerve gas, sarin, together with phosgene, tear gas and mustard gas, have also been dumped."

This is a true environmental disaster and this is just one of many such incidents.

GOOD SCIENCE

You may be wondering whether there is any good science on microplastics. Fortunately, the answer is yes.

Article 1 – Worm

"Biouptake in worms was lower by 76% when PCBs were associated with polypropylene compared to sediment. The presence of microplastics in sediments had an overall impact of reducing bioavailability and transfer of HOCs to sediment-ingesting organisms. Since the vast majority of sediment and suspended particles in the environment are natural organic and inorganic materials, pollutant transfer through particle ingestion will be dominated by these particles and not microplastics. Therefore, these results support the conclusion that in most cases the transfer of organic pollutants to aquatic organisms from microplastic in the diet is likely a small contribution compared to other natural pathways of exposure."

B. Beckingham, U. Ghosh, Differential bioavailability of polychlorinated biphenyls associated with environmental particles: Microplastic in comparison to wood, coal and biochar, Environmental Pollution 220, 150-158, 2017

They noted that microplastics absorb poisons and protected the worms. They also noted that the fraction of microplastics worms eat is negligible.

Article 2 – Drinking water

"Humans have ingested microplastics and other particles in the environment for decades with no related indication of adverse health effects. In addition, drinking-water treatment is effective at removing particles."

Microplastics in Drinking Water Report, World Health Organization (WHO) 2019

"The substantial margin between a theoretical conservative exposure to a range of chemical contaminants detected in microplastics through drinking-water and the level at which no or limited adverse effects were seen, indicates there is a low health concern for chemicals associated with microplastics."

Microplastics in drinking-water, World Health Organization (WHO), 2019

Article 3 – Absorbing toxins

It is often stated that PCBs and heavy metals could be concentrated and transported by microplastics. Even if we assume that is true, we need to ask where the PCBs and heavy metals come from? Toxins in the oceans come from the intentional discharge of untreated industrial effluent into our waterways (i.e., it is chemical "litter" caused by humans). The problem is not to do with plastics themselves; rather, it is caused by people and easily solved by proper, strictly enforced regulations. The study found that plastic trapped toxins present in the ocean, thereby protecting fish. Even when the fish ate the plastic particles, the toxins remained inside the plastic and passed through the fish harmlessly.

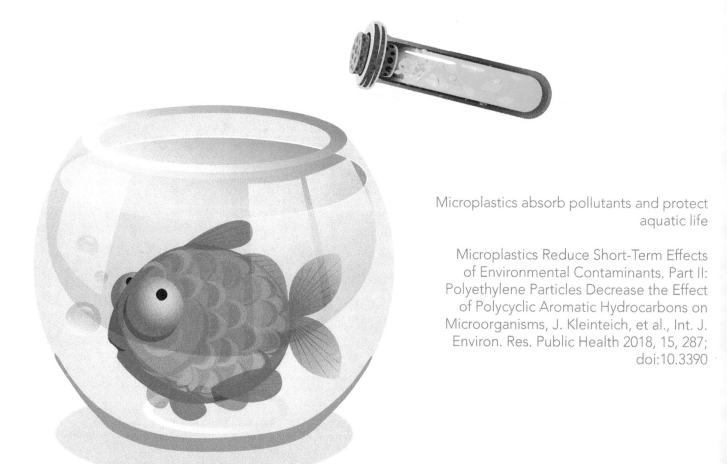

Microplastics absorb pollutants and protect aquatic life

Microplastics Reduce Short-Term Effects of Environmental Contaminants. Part II: Polyethylene Particles Decrease the Effect of Polycyclic Aromatic Hydrocarbons on Microorganisms, J. Kleinteich, et al., Int. J. Environ. Res. Public Health 2018, 15, 287; doi:10.3390

CONCLUSIONS

Microplastics are in our oceans and they should not be there. That much is clear. They have been studied in great detail, so we know what kinds of plastics are present and in what concentrations. Fortunately, these plastics are mainly PE and PP, which we know to be safe. For example, we eat our food out of PE Ziploc® bags and out of PP Tupperware® containers.

People have expressed concern because certain articles claim that microplastics are harmful, either in themselves, or that they release toxic substances. However, there is no credible scientific evidence for either of these claims. Instead, it turns out that these studies were junk science. Other more professional studies showed that microplastics can indeed absorb toxins from the ocean, but that they trap those toxins, thereby protecting marine life.

You may be wondering whether the microplastics will be there forever or if they will degrade over time. In the next chapter, we will look at the degradation of plastics, so we can know what to expect.

Lie # 4 – Microplastics are toxic or release toxins.

Truth – There is no credible evidence that microplastics are toxic, and they actually help protect us from toxins by absorbing and removing them from seawater.

CHAPTER FIVE
DEGRADATION

DEGRADATION OF PLASTICS

One of the major arguments against plastics is that they last for a thousand years, so therefore we must avoid creating any waste plastic because it will accumulate and be with us forever. That sounds ominous, but is it true?

The first thing to say is that all organic materials degrade. For the layperson, organic means everything based on carbon. Organic materials include apples, meat, wood, paper, cotton, our DNA (a polymer), collagen (a polymer), leaves (made of cellulose, which is a polymer), crude oil and so on. Every person will realize this is true as soon as they consider their own experience. An apple will rot and eventually vanish. Similarly, plastic items we use degrade and fail because they are also organic materials.

Many people will remember the original plastic garden chairs. They were made of polypropylene (PP), and after some months in the sun, they would turn white and brittle and break due to microcracks on their surface. Sunlight was enough to destroy these chairs in a matter of months.

I read an article about museum curators who were frustrated that Neil Armstrong's iconic spacesuit was degrading and they were powerless to stop the plastic and rubber parts from crumbling. Think about that for a moment. A spacesuit carefully kept out of sunlight and at room temperature, yet still it degrades. In the end, the Smithsonian raised over $700,000 to restore the suit and put it back on display.

The spacesuit was not an isolated case. A good friend of mine was a Plastics Conservator at a London museum and his task was to try to stop the plastic exhibits from falling to pieces. These were all plastic items kept in the cool behind glass, and yet they were degrading in a matter of years or decades.

How the Smithsonian Will Save Neil Armstrong's Spacesuit, Popular Mechanics, October 2015

1000-YEAR PLASTIC MYTH

The environmental groups tell us that plastics are bad because they don't degrade. They normally give a number of either >450 years or a thousand years for the degradation of plastics. If that were true, it would be wonderful because the plastic on my car would last 1,000 years and I would only have to repaint my house every 1,000 years. The plastic siding on our houses would also last a millennium. If plastic did last that long, then we would see 1000-year warranties on the products we buy. Have you ever seen a 1000-year warranty on a plastic item? Try calling your local Home Depot or Lowe's and ask what plastic products offer a 1000-year warrantee. Your call may well be met with hysterical laughter. No sensible person believes that plastics last that long. We know that from our own experience, so why do people believe the 1000-year myth? Would you rather believe your own eyes or some anonymous blogger?

THE REALITY

As a plastic materials expert, I know how much effort is put into preventing the degradation of plastics, but the public doesn't realize just how unstable they are. Those plastic PP garden chairs I just mentioned now last over a decade rather than months because chemists have developed additives called stabilizers, or antioxidants, to help protect plastic from the sun, heat, and oxygen in the air. Every competent plastics expert knows this. There are whole conferences devoted to the topic. There is a journal called Polymer Degradation and Stability (published by Elsevier) filled with thousands of articles about it. There are many books as well. Claiming that plastics are stable is like arguing a bowling ball will fall upward when you drop it. It's just not true.

Polypropylene plastic garden chairs severely degraded by sunlight

You may have seen me on CBS's 60 Minutes with Scott Pelley talking about PP medical mesh implanted into people. Such mesh is used for vaginal repair and also for hernias. A class-action lawsuit resulted when 100,000 women reported problems and similar lawsuits sprang up from men with hernia mesh. A key topic was the stability of polypropylene. The mesh needs to last 60 years, but calculations showed it would only last 2-4 years before degrading. During that expert witness work, I collected about 100 articles on the stability of PP and other polymers. It is known with certainty that PP without stabilizer loses strength and fails in about a year at room temperature. Only through the addition of antioxidants does it gain enough stability to become useful. The plastic appears stable to us but only because the stabilizer is protecting it.

Consider the fact that the global market for polymer stabilizers is well over six billion dollars a year. That is a truly stupendous amount of money, and companies would not be spending billions on such additives if polymers really were infinitely stable. No, they would simply avoid the additives and save themselves some money. This one number alone should be enough to convince most people that plastics are inherently unstable and only survive due to the addition of stabilizers.

Polymer Stabilizer Market by Type (Antioxidant, Light Stabilizer, Heat Stabilizer), End-use Industry (Packaging, Automotive, Building & Construction, Consumer Goods), and Region - Global Forecast to 2022 – Markets and Markets Report CH 5459, July 2017

DO THE EXPERIMENT

Environmentalists tell us, with no proof at all, that plastics will last up to 1,000 years in the environment. How can they know that when plastics have only been around for less than 100 years? They can't.

The best way to be sure about stability is to do experiments, and recently some scientists tested a standard polyethylene bag in air outdoors to see what would happen. Nine months later, it had lost all of its strength and disintegrated into tiny fragments. One thousand years? No, nine months.

Imogen E. Napper, Richard C. Thompson. Environmental Deterioration of Biodegradable, Oxo-biodegradable, Compostable, and Conventional Plastic Carrier Bags in the Sea, Soil, and Open-Air Over a 3-Year Period. Environmental Science & Technology, 2019

This is an important point and it is against everything we have been told. In such cases, it is worthwhile to present more than one peer-reviewed article to prove the point beyond doubt. So, here is a quote from another scientific article on two types of polyethylene, polypropylene and an oxo-degradable product (meaning a polyolefin with a chemical catalyst added to make it degrade even faster):

"This study shows that the real durability of olefin polymers may be much shorter than centuries, as in less than one year the mechanical properties of all samples decreased virtually to zero, as a consequence of severe oxidative degradation, that resulted in substantial reduction in molar mass accompanied by a significant increase in content of carbonyl groups. PP and the oxo-bio HDPE/LLDPE blend degraded very rapidly, whereas HDPE and LLDPE degraded more slowly, but significantly in a few months."

T. Ojeda et al., Degradability of linear polyolefins under natural weathering, Polymer Degradation and Stability 96, 703-707 2011

They found that all of the plastic bags, including a standard polyethylene grocery bag, disintegrated in less than a year. You may be wondering what becomes of those pieces. They become smaller and smaller until the plastic was converted to carbon dioxide and water. However, that's not what the lobbyists tell us. They like to claim that plastic never truly degrades but just fragments into microplastic. Why would plastic degrade to a certain size and then suddenly stop? That makes no sense because it isn't true. In fact, we know that plastics degrade faster and faster, the smaller they get because it is easier for oxygen to get inside. Once again, their claim is not backed by science. We know for sure what PE and PP degrade into because it had been studied for decades. We look at that in more detail in the following section.

PLASTICS MAKE GREENHOUSE GAS

Interestingly, an environmental scientist made the claim that plastics are degrading to release greenhouse gas. The article received a lot of media coverage.

Degrading plastics 'release greenhouse gases', study shows

Researchers in Hawaii have found some common plastics release methane as they break down, which effectively warms the atmosphere.

Degrading plastics 'release greenhouse gases', study shows, Oliver Buckley, Sky News August 2nd 2018

The scientist measured the gases coming from polyethylene as it degrades and when she saw carbon dioxide and methane, she declared it to be a previously unrecognized source of global warming gas. Here is what she said:

"Our results show that plastics represent a heretofore unrecognized source of climate-relevant trace gases that are expected to increase as more plastic is produced and accumulated in the environment"

Production of methane and ethylene from plastic in the environment, S.-J. Royer et al., PLoS ONE 13(8): e0200574

Trees, leaves, and plants degrade and give off the same gases as plastics do

Think about how ironic this is. The green lobbyists first tell us that plastic doesn't degrade, or if it does, it just fragments but cannot chemically degrade. Then, when they measure the chemical degradation of plastic into gasses, instead of saying "Hurrah, it does degrade after all!" they say it's terrible news, as it will lead to more global warming. So, which is it? Do they want it to degrade or don't they? Apparently, it doesn't matter to them; they just blame plastic either way. This is typical of people who don't care about the truth but are instead determined to demonize a material no matter what the evidence is.

Environmental groups tell us that plastics never truly degrade and instead they form small fragments. They also tell us that synthetic plastics do not biodegrade. Both of these claims are made without evidence and are, in fact, lies because the science shows otherwise. Here is a quote from a detailed review article on the topic:

> "The ultimate products of degradation are CO_2, H_2O, and biomass under aerobic conditions. Anaerobic microorganisms can also degrade these polymers under anoxic conditions."

Arutchelvi et al., Biodegradation of polyethylene and polypropylene, Indian Journal of Biotechnology, 7, pp 9-22 2008

SOME PERSPECTIVE

Should we share their concern that plastic degrades to create greenhouse gases? As with most topics, a little perspective is valuable. I searched to see what other materials degrade to give those same gases. Want to take a guess? Here's what I found:

"Our data strongly suggest that the terrestrial vegetation sampled, including trees, shrubs, herbs, grasses, a sedge and a fern, can emit CH_4, CO, C_2H_4 and C_3H_8 from leaves when exposed to spectrally weighted UV levels equivalent to ambient levels of UV observed outside."

Emission of methane, carbon monoxide, carbon dioxide and short-chain hydrocarbons from vegetation foliage under ultraviolet irradiation, W. T. Fraser et al. Plant, Cell and Environment 2015 38, 980–989

That's a direct quote from an article and it's saying that the degradation of every tree, shrub, herb, grass, and leaf gives off the exact same gases that plastic does. Would these so-called environmentalists also propose banning trees and all the other vegetation in the world? Why not? After all, they are giving off the exact same gases that plastics do, only in vastly greater amounts. This reinforces the point that all organic materials degrade fairly readily and produce similar gases. You might say that plastics are made from fossil fuel, so when they degrade there is a net increase in atmospheric carbon dioxide. However, we have already seen from LCA studies that plastics create a net reduction in overall carbon dioxide release.

WHERE DID THE "1,000 YEARS" COME FROM?

As we know, environmentalists usually quote plastics as lasting >450 years or 1,000 years. Although we know for certain that is plain wrong, and although they never cite a single scientific article to back up their claim, I decided to look to see if I could find the source of the claim. I searched for quite some time, trying to see if anyone had ever given numbers like those. Eventually, I found one book and one article. Notice that I didn't brush them under the carpet. Some environmentalists cite a book by Martha Gorman as proof for their statement. This is what the book says:

> "Many plastics take as long as 500 years to decompose."

It is crucial to note that the book provides no reference to any science to support that statement. As far as I can tell, Gorman just made it up. It's pure fiction. Anyone can make up a statement, but it is unwise to believe statements that are not backed by evidence.

Environmental Hazards: Marine Pollution, M. Gorman, ABC-Clio Inc., 1993

Among hundreds of articles showing that plastics degrade rapidly, I found just one article estimating stability over 100 years. It deals with high-density polyethylene geomembrane (GM) barriers for municipal solid waste (MSW) landfills. They state:

> "Based on the currently available data, the service life for HDPE GM in MSW landfill is estimated to be about 160 years for a primary liner at 35°C and greater than 600 years for a secondary GM provided it is at a temperature of less than 20°C."

R. K. Rowe, Long-term performance of contaminant barrier systems, Géotechnique 55, No. 9, 631–678 2005

Why was their estimate much longer than every other estimated lifetime for polyethylene? There are several reasons. Firstly, geomembranes are designed to last for decades, so they contain vastly more antioxidant (stabilizer) than any other plastic product. The other reason is that Rowe estimated the lifetime using what we now know to be a faulty method. They chose to use the Arrhenius equation, but we now know that the Arrhenius equation doesn't work for estimation of polymer lifetimes. The Arrhenius equation drastically overestimates the time to failure and that is why it is no longer used.

M. Celina, K. T. Gillen, R. A. Assink, Accelerated aging and lifetime prediction: Review of non-Arrhenius behaviour due to two competing processes, Polymer Degradation and Stability 90 395-404 2005

So, we can now understand why he predicted unrealistically long lifetimes for the membrane. He used an equation that is not valid. That's not all, though. His own observations revealed rapid degradation of the polyethylene geomembrane. He noted that the parts of the membrane exposed to the elements were cracked after just 14 years. It was only the parts that were buried deep in the landfill that degraded slowly. As we will see in a later section, nothing degrades quickly when buried deep in a landfill. Even food and paper don't degrade under those conditions because there's not enough oxygen down there for bacteria and oxidation to break them down.

In another study, some researchers went to the trouble of digging up PE pipes that had been buried for 30 years. The HDPE pipes were designed to last 50 years, but they were not sure whether the pipes would make it, so they dug them up after 30 years to check whether they would last another 20 years. They were relieved to find that, although some slight changes had occurred, they were reasonably confident the pipes would reach 50 years of service life. If plastics experts really did believe PE and PP lasted 500 or 1000 years, they would not spend time and money digging up pipes to see if they would make it to 50 years.

A. Frank, G. Pinter, R. W. Lang, Prediction of the remaining lifetime of polyethylene pipes after up to 30 years in use, Polymer Testing 28, 737–745 2009

STABILIZING PLASTICS

You may be wondering why plastics can look just fine when they are so unstable. That is an excellent question. PP, for example, is so unstable that they spray stabilizer on it the instant they make it to prevent attack by oxygen in the air. Once the stabilizer is in the PP, it will be completely protected as long as there is stabilizer left. This gives the impression that the plastic is stable when, in actuality, it is not. It gives us an illusion of stability.

Polypropylene Handbook, E. P. Moore, Hanser Publishers, NY, NY, USA 1996

How do antioxidants work and what are they? Think about cutting into an apple. The apple turns brown quickly due to oxidation. But if you put some lemon juice on the cut apple, it will not turn brown because there is an antioxidant, Vitamin C, in the lemon juice. The apple will, however, turn brown as soon as the Vitamin C has all been used up. It's the same with plastics. They look fine until the antioxidant is all used up, then they oxidize, discolour, lose strength, and fail.

Vitamin C is not a good antioxidant for plastics because it doesn't dissolve in them. Vitamin E, on the other hand, is an excellent antioxidant made by nature to protect oily substances in seeds and plants. Vitamin E works very well in plastics and synthetic antioxidants with very similar chemistry are commonly used in many plastics. They are known as hindered phenols and they work by reacting with free radicals that would otherwise destroy the plastic.

WHAT ABOUT OTHER PLASTICS?

Another common plastic is PET. Here is a quote from a study on the degradation of PET:

"In laboratory experiments studying PET degradation, a life expectancy of PET bottles was predicted under 100% humidity of 27 and 93 years. Whereas Muller et al. in his review paper based on the above-mentioned studies predicted the general lifetime of PET ranging from 16 to 48 years."

C. Ioakeimidis et al., The degradation potential of PET bottles in the marine environment: An ATR-FTIR based approach, Scientific Reports volume 6, Article number: 23501 2016

These are only estimates, so the workers decided to recover PET bottles from the sea and use the expiry dates printed on the bottles as a rough estimate of the age for each bottle. The PET degraded with clear changes in the chemistry found by infrared spectroscopy. After 15 years in the sea, the characteristic chemical bonds were almost gone, indicating severe degradation. Although the chemistry of PET degradation is completely different compared to PE and PP, we still see that the plastic degrades over a period of years, not centuries or millennia.

SUNLIGHT AND PLASTICS

Let's return to our discussion about how free radicals destroy plastics. If the term "free radical" sounds familiar, it may be because you've heard of it in connection with sunburn. The UV light in sunshine has enough energy to create free radicals, which are extremely reactive. They are capable of damaging your skin and even causing cancer by altering your DNA (remember, DNA is a polymer). It should therefore come as no surprise that the UV light in sunlight also attacks the polymer chains in plastics. Plastics need to be protected from the sun the same way that people do. For example:

1. Keep them out of the sun
2. Use antioxidants that neutralize free radicals
3. Use sun-blocking chemicals or particles that reflect the UV light

For people, we apply sunscreen which contains additives that absorb the UV light or reflect it back. For plastics, we don't lather on sunscreen because we can add the UV blockers inside the plastic. Some of the exact same additives are used. For example, zinc oxide and titanium dioxide are used in sunscreen, in plastics, and in coatings. For car tires, carbon black blocks all light (including UV) and thereby protects the rubber. That same additive is used widely in plastics too.

Y. Hu, J. Xu, Q. Hu, Evaluation of antioxidant potential of aloe vera (Aloe barbadensis miller) extracts, J. Agric. Food Chem., 17;51(26):7788-91, 2003

Polymer scientists know that the UV light in sunlight readily destroys plastics. A recent article showed that even polystyrene, one of the most stable plastics, degrades far more rapidly than scientists previously believed.

"Here, we show that polystyrene is completely photochemically oxidized to carbon dioxide and partially photochemically oxidized to dissolved organic carbon. Lifetimes of complete and partial photochemical oxidation are estimated to occur on centennial and decadal time scales, respectively. These lifetimes are orders of magnitude faster than biological respiration of polystyrene and thus challenge the prevailing assumption that polystyrene persists in the environment for millennia."

C . P. Ward et al, Sunlight Converts Polystyrene to Carbon Dioxide and Dissolved Organic Carbon, Environmental Science & Technology Letters, 6, 669-674 2019

They found that although polystyrene is very unreactive and was thought to persist for thousands of years, it actually degrades completely in decades when exposed to sunlight. It is possible to make the degradation go even faster, if so desired, by using additives to increase its light-sensitivity.

In the Sea, Not All Plastic Lasts Forever

Polystyrene, a common ocean pollutant, decomposes in sunlight much faster than thought, a new study finds.

William J. Broad, New York Times, October 11th 2019

PLASTICS IN A LANDFILL

It seems clear that some people are determined to demonize plastic no matter what the facts are and no matter how illogical their arguments. Environmentalists say plastics don't degrade in a landfill, and that's true because landfills are not designed to encourage degradation. It's well-known that even food and paper don't degrade in a landfill because there's not enough oxygen present. Here is a quote from an article on this subject:

"There are the 40-year-old hot dogs, perfectly preserved beneath dozens of strata of waste, and the head of lettuce still in pristine condition after 25 years. But the hands-down winner, the one that still makes him shake his head in disbelief, is an order of guacamole he recently unearthed. Almost as good as new, it sat next to a newspaper apparently thrown out the same day. The date was 1967."

William Grimes, Seeking the Truth in Refuse, August 13th 1992, New York Times

People have recovered carrots, steaks, avocados, and more from landfills. Even after burial for years, they look pristine. Decades-old newspapers can still be read without any problem.

William L. Rathje, Cullen Murphy, Rubbish!: The Archaeology of Garbage, HarperCollins 1992

Saying that plastics don't degrade in a landfill is not relevant because nothing does. A study concluded "only 30%, of the carbon from paper and 0-3% of the carbon from wood are ever emitted as landfill gas" and the rest remains as sequestered carbon. That's probably a good thing; otherwise, we would have a lot more greenhouse gas in the atmosphere. Landfills are designed to be a carbon sink—i.e., they lock away carbon preventing it from being given off as CO_2.

J. A. Micales & K. E. Skog, International Biodeterioration & Biodegradation Vol. 39, No. 2-3, 145-158 1997

Landfills are designed to trap carbon, not to encourage degradation

Despite the low oxygen levels, PP actually degrades rather rapidly, as shown below, if it is not buried too deeply.

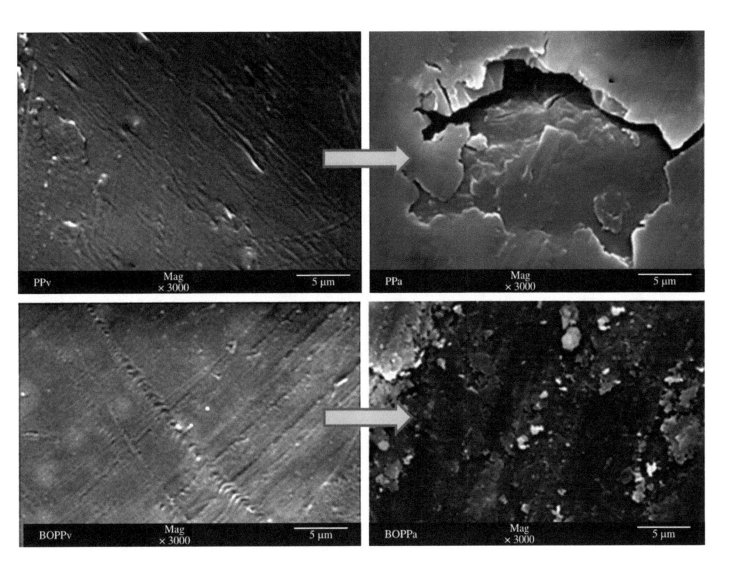

Degradation Study of Polypropylene (PP) and Bioriented Polypropylene (BOPP) in the Environment, C. Longo et al., Materials Research., 14(4) p 442-448 2011

It is unfair to criticize plastics for not degrading in a landfill because landfills are designed to prevent degradation that leads to release of carbon dioxide gas. Plastics are organic materials and degrade at rates similar to other organic materials like leaves, food, cotton, and so on. Polymers also degrade completely in the environment via similar chemical reactions to other organic materials. The following table summarizes the degradation of various materials under different conditions.

Material	Degrades in Soil?	Degrades in Landfill?	Degradation releases CO_2 & methane?	Green According to LCA?
PE or PP Film	Yes 1-3 years	No >100 years	Yes	Yes
Paper	Yes 1-3 years	No >100 years	Yes	No: 3-4x worse than PE & PP
PLA or PHB Bioplastic Film	Yes 1-3 years	No >100 years	Yes	No: worse than PE and PP
Food e.g. carrots, steak	Yes 1-3 years	No >100 years	Yes	Not applicable

Material degradation rate and consequences compared

CONCLUSIONS

There is no basis for the claims that plastics last for a thousand years. In fact, the reverse is true. Plastics are unstable materials and scientists have laboured hard to improve their stability. A common grocery bag disintegrates and vanishes in less than one year outdoors. It is true that some plastic parts can be made to last longer but that is only possible by adding large amounts of stabilizers. Plastics like PE and PP can be fine-tuned to last a year or much longer depending on the application.

Lie #5 – Plastic last hundreds or thousands of years in the environment.

Truth – Standard plastics degrade outdoors in a few years, or even sooner, unless they are stabilized.

CHAPTER SIX
CORRUPTION

CORRUPTION, DISTRACTION, AND GREED

Members of the public, people like you and me, don't normally have the time or the training to delve deeply into the global topics that concern us. Instead, we rely on governments, NGOs, and corporations to sort out the facts and tell us what's what.

As we have seen, that system is not working. People rely on environmental groups in good faith, but when we check what they have recommended, it's not only wrong but clearly harmful to the environment. We, the misled public, make demands based on this incorrect advice. This chapter investigates the systems that have let us down so badly.

HOW CAN THEY BE SO WRONG?

We have seen that Greenpeace consistently take stances that are opposed to the best science and most respected scientists from around the world. There are various possible explanations. Perhaps they are utterly incompetent, or maybe it is because they do not have proper scientists in their ranks, so they are unable to tell what is right and what is wrong. Alternatively, it could be that they only care about the money from our donations. It is very difficult to be sure of motives, but one conclusion is very clear. These people take $400 million a year in donations from the public, given in good faith, and they appear to have been too lazy to spend one minute to do a Google search for "LCA plastic bag". That is unacceptable for an organization that claims to be helping the environment.

As a scientist, I found it hard to fathom how this could come about. Being unfamiliar with the inner workings of environmental NGOs, I decided to learn from someone who knows Greenpeace intimately. Patrick Moore is described as a Greenpeace founder and has published a book explaining why he split from the organization. He is also a PhD chemist, like me, so I thought his perspective would be illuminating. I highly encourage you to read his book because it explains what the science says about how to preserve our planet and shape a sustainable future.

Dr Moore explains that Greenpeace started out with passion and good intentions. They had some early success with their provocative demonstrations against whaling, for example, and before long they were taking in $100 million a year in donations and searching for new topics to address. He had this to say about why he left:

"Despite my best efforts the movement abandoned science and logic somewhere in the mid-1980s, just as society was adopting the more reasonable positions on environmental issues."

Dr Patrick Moore - Greenpeace Founder

P . Moore, Confessions of a Greenpeace Dropout: The Making of a Sensible Environmentalist, Beatty Street Publishing Inc., Vancouver B. C. Canada 2010

He goes on to give specific examples of their actions and how they created large-scale suffering and death for example, through their attacks on GMO food as detailed in the next section.

GMO FOOD

Genetically modified food has been created to withstand droughts, to need less pesticide, and to generate additional nutrients, such as vitamin A, to prevent malnutrition in developing countries. One such development is called Golden Rice, which gets its colour from the pro-vitamin A (beta-carotene) it produces to reduce the risks for infection, diseases, and blindness in developing countries.

Here are his words:

> "For nearly 15 years now, we have had the knowledge to eliminate malnutrition in the world, especially in the rice-eating cultures where nutrient deficiencies affect tens of millions of people. But groups like Greenpeace and the World Wildlife Fund have blocked these advances by promoting fear in the public and by supporting regulations that stifle research, development, and adoption of genetically modified crops. They are effectively condemning millions to suffering and death for the sake of superstition. Surely, this can't seriously be called environmentalism."
>
> Dr. Patrick Moore – Greenpeace Founder

Golden Rice is just one example, but Greenpeace are opposed to genetically modified food even though it has been proven safe and even though 107 (now 151) Nobel laureates wrote to them in support of it. Even if Greenpeace have no one qualified to make a judgement on the merits of the science, how can they be arrogant enough to think their opinion is worth more than that of over a hundred laureates? There is no excuse for blocking all forms of progress, when humanity depends on such breakthroughs for its survival.

107 Nobel laureates sign letter blasting Greenpeace over GMOs

Joel Achenbach, Washington Post, June 30th 2016

When major companies want to make sure they make sound decisions, they form a scientific advisory board where top scientists give them guidance. If Greenpeace really did care about doing what's right, they should set up such a board. It is inexpensive to do, and with hundreds of millions of our dollars, they can certainly afford it.

ATTACKING THE PLASTICS INDUSTRY

Some years ago, I was visiting a large manufacturer of polyethylene and polypropylene. While having coffee before the meeting, they mentioned that Greenpeace had published a piece in the newspaper claiming that the plastics manufacturer was polluting the environment, and he proceeded to recount the story. The company had been shocked and invited Greenpeace to talk with them. The Greenpeace representatives introduced their chemist and my friend asked him where he had studied. He replied "Lund". My friend said that was a coincidence as he had also studied there. Naturally, my friend asked who the Greenpeace chemist's professors were in case they knew some of the same people. Strangely, their chemist was unable to name even one of his professors. I can tell you, I had as good a time as anyone at university, but I can still name my professors! Eventually, the meeting commenced, and the plastics manufacturer expressed concern that they had somehow done something wrong. They asked what had prompted the article, and Greenpeace said that they actually had no evidence of wrongdoing; they had simply written the article to see what reaction they could stir up. The plastics company was not impressed. They pointed out that the livelihoods of hundreds of employees and their families rely on the plastics factory and that it is irresponsible to just make up stories.

GREENPEACE CREDIBILITY LOST

That was quite a story, which I why I remember it to this day. I also remember wondering why they didn't sue Greenpeace for libel. It seems that Greenpeace has not changed their ways, because a company in the forestry industry called Resolute recently sued Greenpeace for unjustly targeting them and spreading lies. Can you guess what Greenpeace's defence in court was? They made no attempt to support their claim with evidence or science. Instead they said that their statements were just made up and that no one was expected to take them seriously! The problem is that the public does take their statements seriously. Greenpeace receives hundreds of millions in donations from people and companies who believe their statements, which we now know to be pure fiction. It seems Patrick Moore was correct when he pointed out they had abandoned science and simply "make stuff up".

Greenpeace admits its attacks on forest products giant were 'non-verifiable statements of subjective opinion'

Now Greenpeace says it never intended people to take its words about Resolute's logging practices as literal truth

Greenpeace admits its attacks on forest products giant were 'non-verifiable statements of subjective opinion',
Peter Kuitenbrouwer, National Post, March 2nd 2017

It seems that governments are starting to wake up to Greenpeace's behaviour because their non-profit charity status has been revoked in India, New Zealand, and Canada.

Canada Leaves Greenpeace Red-Faced

Canada Leaves Greenpeace Red-Faced, Institute of Economic Affairs, July 11th 1999

The article went on to say:

"It's official: Greenpeace Serves No Public Purpose"

and

"Revenue Canada, the tax-collecting arm of the government, has refused to recognize the new Greenpeace Environmental Foundation as a charity, saying its activities have 'no public benefit' and that lobbying to shut down industries could send people into poverty."

A friend remarked that I seemed upset about this. How would you feel if you trusted a babysitter to look after your kids and the babysitter beat them instead? That's exactly what some of the less scrupulous "green" lobby groups are doing. They take our money and we feel like we've done a good deed, but instead, they spend our money on perpetuating themselves and lobbying for actions proven to harm the environment. It is time for this to stop. They have been exposed as frauds and we need to cut off their funding so that they cannot spread any more lies or indoctrinate our children.

"They just make stuff up".

Dr. Patrick Moore – Greenpeace Founder

Patrick Moore - The Power of Truth, keynote address to the Economic Education Association of Alberta's 6th annual "Freedom School" conference, on "Things that Matter: An Agenda for Alberta" available on YouTube

I should mention that I bear no animosity toward Greenpeace and I don't believe I've ever met anyone representing them. I am using them as one example of a so-called "environmental group" who appear to be doing more harm than good. Other environmental NGOs are doing a much better job and deserve praise.

So-called environmentalists are killing our planet with bad advice and lies

How much damage can misinformation really do? Here is one example of misinformation causing harm. Before the 1990s, parents were still being advised by doctors to put babies to sleep on their front, even though that was contrary to what clinical research studies advised. The result was that, for many years, there was an unnecessarily high occurrence of sudden infant death, also known as cot death. Spreading bad advice that was contrary to the science at the time caused tens of thousands of deaths. It was said that heeding the scientific advice earlier:

"...would have led to earlier recognition of the risks of sleeping on the front and might have prevented over 10,000 infant deaths in the UK and at least 50,000 in Europe, the USA, and Australasia."

Even after scientists proved the danger and offered the solution, people maintained the practice for two decades more. I hope this illustrates how false information can spread unchallenged and that even when it is disproven, people do not want to change.

R. Gilbert et al., Infant sleeping position and the sudden infant death syndrome: systematic review of observational studies and historical review of recommendations from 1940 to 2002, International Journal of Epidemiology, 34:874–887 2005

Let us not make the same mistake when it comes to plastics and our environment. We have decades of solid science showing us what is good and what is bad. The message is clear. Plastics are usually the best solution and we need to embrace that while at the same time reducing, reusing, and recycling.

WHY DO WE FALL FOR THE LIES?

As the "green movement" has become so strong, I wondered why people accepted the false narrative so readily. Why are people so passionately against plastic, even without any hard proof?

VIRTUE-SIGNALLING AND MORAL GRANDSTANDING

I'm not a psychologist, so I checked the opinion of someone who is. I found the words of Professor Jordan Peterson very illuminating.

"Generally…the way people avoid their own personal issues is by adopting pseudo-moralistic stances on large-scale social issues, so that they look good to their friends and their neighbours."

Professor Jordan Peterson

Jordan Peterson Destroys Q&A, ABC Australia, 25th February 2019 on YouTube

There is research to back up Professor Peterson's claims. A recent article describes moral grandstanding:

"Moral grandstanding is the use of moral talk to seek social status."

J. B. Grubbs et al., Moral grandstanding in public discourse: Status-seeking motives as a potential explanatory mechanism in predicting conflict, PLoS ONE 14(10): e0223749, October 2019

A related and more common term is "virtue-signalling" whereby someone expresses an opinion to make themselves look good to others. I found this article excerpt rather insightful:

'Virtue-signaling' – the putdown that has passed its sell-by date, David Shariatmadari,
The Guardian 20th January 2016

This reminds me of all the cries of people saying how much they hate plastics. Could it be that most of these people are actually just touting such views in an attempt to impress others? If so, that could have serious implications. For example, perhaps the perceived market for green products is an illusion because the public doesn't actually care as much as they claim to. I have personally seen companies develop green products only to discover that customers would not pay even a few per cent extra for them.

It seems then that we espouse lofty moralistic goals to look good to others. Of course, that may be fine as long as we cause no harm. But there is harm. We as consumers and voters are demanding that we use less plastic because we've been told that's a good thing. We demand bag bans. We say we will spend more for "green" products. The problem is that all of those demands harm, rather than help, the environment.

People who truly care will read this book and check the facts to make wise decisions for a sustainable future. I find that many people are persuaded when they finally learn the truth. Some people cannot be reached by evidence and logic, which means that their actions will end up causing harm instead of good. That is rather unfortunate for them, and for us too. Perhaps their strong beliefs are such a part of their identity that they cannot accept any threat to those beliefs, no matter how persuasive.

In my experience, there is indeed a small fraction of fanatics who scream loudly that they will never change their mind about plastics being evil. They make passionate, hate-filled attacks against all who question their views, but they absolutely refuse to consider any evidence that is presented to them.

A thought occurs to me when confronted by such fanatics. If these people, who claim to be environmentalists, really believed what they say, they would all hand back their plastic computers, plastic cell phones, plastic-enabled cars and go live in a cave somewhere. They would be unable to post their hate-filled comments online with no electricity, because wires need plastic to insulate them.

This is where someone genuinely against plastics would be living

They would have no running water, because plastic pipes deliver it. Do we see these passionate crusaders doing that? No, we do not. Why? Because they are virtue-signalling, grandstanding liars. They talk the talk, but they don't walk the walk. Once you realise that they are loud but not genuine, they are easy to ignore.

COMPANIES, GOVERNMENTS, AND ACADEMIA

We speak and companies listen. There are now countless products made specifically to cater to public demands. Some of these products are actually green, but many of them are falsely advertised as green, so how are we to know which are real and which are nonsense? I will give some examples.

GOVERNMENT BANS

One common response to a problem is to impose a ban. This approach has a certain appeal. When you impose a ban, you are seen to have taken action, and politicians like that. Bans do have a place, but often they are not the best option.

When cars were first introduced, there were many accidents. There is some debate about the earliest accident, but here is a description of one of them:

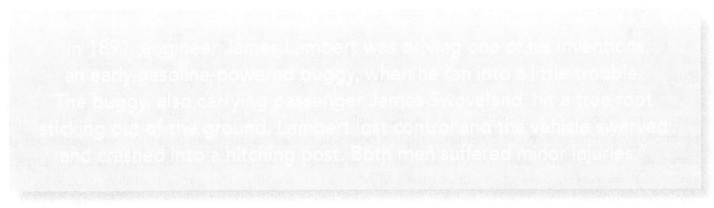

"In 1891, engineer James Lambert was driving one of his inventions, an early gasoline-powered buggy, when he ran into a little trouble. The buggy, also carrying passenger James Swoveland, hit a tree root sticking out of the ground. Lambert lost control and the vehicle swerved and crashed into a hitching post. Both men suffered minor injuries."

When and Where Was the First Car Accident? Matt Soniak, Mental Floss, December 6th 2012

They could have banned cars as a knee-jerk response. Instead, it was recognized that cars are useful and that the answer was to create proper rules and regulations plus a better infrastructure in the form of roads and signs. Today we don't have tree roots jutting up out of dirt roads. The problem was solved without a ban.

Early adopters of electricity had accidents, but we didn't ban electricity despite the clear danger it can pose. Similarly, early use of x-rays caused accidents but now they are used safely on a routine basis. Here is a quote from an article about early electrical deaths caused by x-ray machines:

"We found 51 fatal and 62 non-fatal but serious electrical accidents. Most of them occurred between 1920 and 1940 and involved transformers that provided output currents well above the threshold for the induction of ventricular fibrillation. The accidents led to recommendations and regulations to improve safety for operators and patients, and spurred manufacturers to technical developments that culminated in fully electrically shockproof systems by 1935."

G. J. Kemerink et al., Forgotten electrical accidents and the birth of shockproof X-ray systems, Insights Imaging, 4:513–523 2013

Early problems were recognized and quickly solved by proper regulations and design.

Every new technology, including plastics, has initial problems, but the solution is not to ban the technology. Progress is made by embracing the best solutions and then creating the framework so that they can be used responsibly. When it comes to the developed world, this approach has been largely successful. However, developing countries are now going through the same teething problems we had a few decades ago. They have litter issues and pump their waste into the environment, just as we used to do. The countries pumping trash into the oceans are not full of bad people—they are simply struggling to deal with something new. Fortunately, it will be easier for them to solve their problems because we have already shown them the template to copy.

Earlier, we showed data indicating that banning plastic bags has had serious health consequences because the alternative bag materials are less green and reusable bags can become contaminated with deadly bacteria.

Straws have been banned and replaced with paper straws, which are worse for the environment, by bamboo straws that leach toxic chemicals, and metal straws. A woman was killed by reusable metal straw and that was a preventable accident. Unjustly demonizing plastic straws has killed at least one person already. Sadly, the women with the metal straw thought she was helping the environment because she had been fed the same lies that you and I have been.

Here is a headline about a government ban on microplastic beads in face wash:

Government urged to ban microbeads in bathroom products over plastic pollution damage to marine life

Single shower 'can result in 100,000 plastic particles entering the ocean'

Joel Achenbach, Washington Post, June 30th 2016

That article in The Independent stated:

Government urged to ban microbeads in bathroom products over plastic pollution damage to marine life, Loulla-Mae Eleftheriou-Smith, The Independent, August 24th 2016

The UK government banned plastic microbeads on this basis. That must be great news, right? Well, let's look at the statement piece by piece. It says microplastics do not biodegrade. They are made of polyethylene and science shows they do biodegrade and also degrade chemically by oxidation. So, the first statement is untrue. I looked for information about filtration of microplastics and found a presentation from the Centre for Ecology and Hydrology entitled Microplastics in Freshwater Systems by Alice Horton. She states that the efficiency of microplastics removal in three separate peer-reviewed studies was 99%, 95% and 97%.

A. Horton, Microplastics in Freshwater Systems, Centre for Ecology and Hydrology, Natural Environment Research Council, UK

She is saying that, according to the science, water treatment removes almost all microplastics. So, the second part of the statement from the Independent is also wrong.

Lastly, the Independent piece said that it's feared that microplastics can carry toxins. However, numerous studies show that microplastics end up sequestering toxins and holding them inside, thereby purifying water and protecting aquatic life. You may be wondering what happens if the toxin-containing plastic is ingested, for example, by a fish. That has been studied, and it was shown that 90-100% of the toxic chemicals stay inside the microplastic particles. The particles actually shield the fish from harm. This is a very important finding, but have you seen a headline about that? No? Why not? I'll tell you why. Scary stories sell better than happy ones. That's why the news on TV is full of all the worst events they can muster up.

What do these unrealistic microplastic articles show us? First, someone made up a set of lies, then they presented them to the government who didn't bother to check the facts and instead pressured industry to act. Then finally they banned the product. Lastly, the environmental groups claim a victory. Once that is done, it is time for the environmental group to make up another imaginary problem and start the process all over again.

The US government made the same mistake. On December 28, 2015, President Obama signed the Microbead-Free Waters Act of 2015, banning plastic microbeads in cosmetics and personal care products. Looking back on it, banning those microbeads was probably a good thing, but as we now see, it was done for all the wrong reasons. This is not the correct way to make progress. We need to call out lies. We must press government to check the facts and only impose actions when they are known to make sense based on those facts.

We speak and governments listen. Let's be honest: governments care a lot more about getting your vote and getting into power than they do about doing what's actually right. We say we want a bag ban, and they are only too happy to deliver. As you now know, it takes 60 seconds on Google to search "LCA plastic bag" and discover that plastic bags are definitely the greenest option. It's not hard, but governments go ahead and implement the ban we asked for, even though it harms the environment to do so. Many such bans have been reversed upon further examination of the facts.

The phrase "be careful what you wish for" seems apt here.

COMPANY BANS

The supermarket chain Iceland tried removing plastic packaging and replacing with paper, but it had to abandon the plan due to food wastage and low customer acceptance.

ITV REPORT 22 July 2019 at 12:04am

Iceland goes bananas after plastic-free packaging woes

Iceland goes bananas after plastic-free packaging woes, ITV Report 22nd July 2019

Their sales plummeted 20%, and I saw someone online ask, "Why do sales matter?" What a silly question. They matter because you can't save the planet if you're out of business. The CEO said this at the time:

> "We can't do anything that will endanger the success of the business, because there's 25,000 jobs depending on it."

It is often the case that customers say they want a green product, but when you offer the green alternative, they don't buy it. This may come down to moral grandstanding whereby people make statements to look good but don't actually mean it when it comes to opening their wallet.

Here is another typical headline where a large company (which should know better) makes a change that harms the environment in order to appease their misinformed customers.

Technology
Nestle Wraps Yes Bar in Paper as It Seeks to Cut Plastic Waste

By Corinne Gretler and Ellen Milligan
July 2, 2019, 5:59 PM EDT

Nestle Wraps Yes Bar in Paper as It Seeks to Cut Plastic Waste, Bloomberg July 2nd 2019

A recent headline highlighted interviews with major supermarket chains. It turns out that the supermarkets are getting rid of plastic due to customer pressure, but at the same time, they realize that these actions actually harm the environment.

Supermarkets bringing in even more damaging packaging in rush to ditch plastic, study finds

Race to find alternatives leads to rise in items creating more greenhouse gases

Jane Dalton, The Independent, January 9th 2019

Supermarkets have also made material changes that were unsuccessful and had to be reversed. It turns out that their customers shout for change but are not actually prepared to change their own buying habits. It would seem that the demand for greener packaging is mainly illusory.

Plastic promises What the grocery sector is really doing about packaging
L. Peake, The Green Alliance Trust, January 2019

COMPANY EXPLOITATION

Companies are only too willing to mislead us and take our money. Look at the Bite Toothpaste pellets as an example. Hopefully, you can now see through this scam.

Vegan toothpaste pill aims to cut plastics in landfills

The product is a pill that comes inside a thick glass bottle with a metal screw cap. That should already be causing alarm bells to ring in your head because metal and glass have a much worse environmental footprint than the plastic that they are replacing.

"Toothpaste, reinvented. The only all-natural, plastic-free way to replace the paste you've used your whole life."

https://bitetoothpastebits.com

The packaging is a cardboard box upon which is printed:

"Zero paste. Zero waste."

Does that sound believable to you? How can a product that comes packaged in glass, metal, and cardboard be "zero waste"? It can't. It's a marketing ploy designed to prey on the gullible. They have replaced a plastic solution with something far worse and then tried to pass it off as a green breakthrough.

Here is another headline:

L'Oréal Is Launching Seed Phytonutrients, a Sustainable Beauty Brand With Paper Packaging

L'Oréal Is Launching Seed Phytonutrients, a Sustainable Beauty Brand With Paper Packaging, Macaela Mackenzie, Allure, April 20th 2018

Large companies have huge sustainability teams and virtually unlimited resources. It is not too much to expect that they type "LCA paper plastic" into Google and check what's green before creating a new product line based on nonsense.

The point is not to put these two companies in the spotlight. There are tens of thousands of examples out there. When someone is trying to pry the money out of our wallets, we need to examine their motives and their claims. What proof to do they give (if any) that they are offering a greener option?

ACADEMIC DECEPTION

Now consider this headline is a popular UK newspaper.

How melting plastic waste could heat homes

Breakthrough means less pollution and lower greenhouse gas emissions

How melting plastic waste could heat homes, The Guardian, Jillian Ambrose, July 20th 2019

The article says:

How melting plastic waste could heat homes, Jillian Ambrose, The Guardian, July 20th 2019

People reposted this "breakthrough" on LinkedIn and I even had emails asking me what I thought about it. Let's take a look. By now you know me well enough that I will not take this at face value but will spend some time to check what the science tells us. Let's start by looking at PE and PP, the two most common plastics.

How much energy is in common plastics like PE and PP? Energy is measured in kilojoules per gram.

Heat released by burning gasoline is 47.3 kJ/g
Heat released by burning diesel is 44.8 kJ/g
Heat released by burning polyethylene is 44.6 kJ/g
Heat released by burning polypropylene is 42.7 kJ/g

PE and PP are as good an energy source as coal

The answer is that, because these polymers have the same chemistry as fuel oils, they burn well and give out the same amount of heat energy.

Heat of Combustion of High Temperature Polymers, Technical Note, US Department of Transportation, DOT/FAA/AR-TN97/8 1998

The peer-reviewed scientific studies report that PE and PP burn cleanly with very low levels of soot generation. So, they are safe to burn as well.

Brooke E. Shemwell & Yiannis A. Levendis, Particulates Generated from Combustion of Polymers (Plastics), Journal of the Air & Waste Management Association, 50:1, 94-102 2000

Next let us consider plastic waste mixtures. A detailed study was done on the combustion of plastic waste mixtures. The workers noted that PE and PP gave the largest amount of energy when burnt but said that those two polymers should be recycled instead whenever possible. Therefore, they removed the PE and PP and burnt the remaining plastic waste. They noted that even with PE and PP absent, burning plastic waste gave off more heat than burning coal.

Costiuc et al., Experimental Investigation on the Heat of Combustion for Solid Plastic Waste Mixtures, Environmental Engineering and Management Journal 14 6, 1295-1302 2015

Now that we have checked the science, let's go back to the article claiming a breakthrough method for converting waste plastic into fuel.

We just talked about how plastic waste can be burnt cleanly as-is and give more energy than we get from the same amount of coal. Now, these university researchers are proposing that instead of doing that, instead we heat the plastic to 1,000°C and convert it into liquid fuel. That is utterly insane because it requires using a lot of heat to convert solid plastic fuel into liquid fuel. Why would you want to start with excellent solid fuel and then spend a large portion of the energy in that fuel to change it into a liquid? It defeats the whole purpose.

This kind of headline attracts readers and the journalists assume it must make sense because someone at a university did the work. That's just not the case. Academics often have no clue about what makes sense in the real world. What they care about it getting publicity and funding for their whacky ideas.

If I had written the headline for their work, it might read something like "Gullible attention-seeking scientists invent process for converting excellent fuel into worse fuel".

I hope that universities will be more careful about what they release to the public and that journalists will do a better job checking these stories with independent experts. I see headlines like that one all the time, and as a scientist, it's clear how ridiculous the claims are but it is not so clear to everyone else. How is a member of the public to tell what's true and what makes sense? It must be difficult, and I hope this book will make a contribution to that effort. Now you should be armed to see through some of the false information that bombards us every day.

As long as companies smell money, governments smell votes, and academics smell funding, they will keep promoting nonsense. A prime example is the hundreds of millions of funding thrown at biopolymers. Perhaps you have seen articles about plastics like PLA, PHB, PHAs and so on. We'll look at that topic next.

BIOPOLYMERS AND BIODEGRADABLE POLYMERS

I'm a plastic materials expert and this is one of the hottest areas at the moment, so you might assume that I am going to promote these plastics as the solution to all our problems. However, that's not the way good scientists work. They don't promote topics for their own convenience. Instead they have to investigate the facts impartially, which is the opposite of what many laypeople do. The layperson often forms an opinion and only reads articles that support their pre-existing view. That tendency is reinforced by the internet whereby our surfing behaviour is tracked, and we are fed only the articles and commercials that the algorithm knows we will like.

I remember my first exposure to biopolymers in 1982, when my stepfather brought home a yellow key fob made of a new polymer called PHB from the chemical company ICI.

ICI weighs marketing of new thermoplastic, Chem. Eng. News Archive, 60 (47) p6 1982

Later came PLA and other biodegradable polymers. They still attract a lot of attention, but do they make sense? Once again, we must turn to LCA studies. What do they say? Every LCA study I have found clearly states that these biodegradable polymers are worse for the environment than standard plastics like PE and PP. So, they are not green at all, despite the marketing claims of the manufacturers.

These plastics have other major problems, too. PLA takes too long to mould, and it softens at such a low temperature that it can't be used in many important applications. PHB is too brittle, so researchers have looked for ways around that. In short, these biodegradable polymers are less green, more expensive, and have worse properties than the plastics we use today. It's no wonder that they have not taken off, even after several decades on the market. One well-known professor was referring to articles with titles such as "plastic cutlery made from PHB" and similar headlines that pop up regularly. He summed it up well when he told me:

"They've made everything out of PHB apart from money."

Meaning, yes, you can make parts out of it, but not a profit. Shortly thereafter, the news broke that the leading producer of PHB/PHA, Metabolix, had abandoned the business.

Metabolix Gives Up On the Bioplastic Business

At the time they said:

PLA has had some limited success but it's main selling points are being green (which it isn't, according to LCA) and being biodegradable, when we know that PE and PP also degrade while being cheaper as well.

I watched professor Norman Billingham's keynote lecture at a conference in Stockholm on biodegradable polymers and he opened by saying something along the lines:

"Biodegrading plastics via composting amounts to releasing all the CO_2 without recovering the energy. Plastics can be replaced, reused, recycled, or burned to recover heat - aerobic biodegradation should be a route of last resort."

Professor Norman Billingham

That is an excellent point. If you use PE and PP, for example, you can recycle and reuse them many times over, then, when you finally have to burn them, you recover all of the energy contained in them. On the other hand, biopolymers degrade slowly in the ground, so we throw away all of that energy they contain. It makes no sense to do it that way.

Major companies have told me that they are against biodegradable packaging. They have considered it but, in the end, they were too worried that it would just encourage bad behaviour. Putting a product in a biodegradable wrapper is like saying, "Don't worry, you can just throw this on the floor when you're finished with it". Although the biodegradable option is there, companies want to encourage responsible behaviour, not the reverse.

I .Nkwachukwu et al, Focus on potential environmental issues on plastic world towards a sustainable plastic recycling in developing countries, International Journal of Industrial Chemistry, 4:34 2013

BIO-BASED FILLERS

In addition to biopolymers, there has been a lot of work putting "green" fillers into plastics. For example, one can mix wood particles (i.e. sawdust) into PE or PP and make plastic decking. There are commercial products based on such formulations that look like wood but have better durability and rot resistance. What about the environmental aspect, though? The problem is that while the starting plastic is recyclable, once you add the sawdust, it is not. The high temperatures used to process the polymer degrade the wood, it starts to turn dark brown and smell bad. So, adding what appears to be a "green filler" turns out to be counterproductive.

How green is wood compared to plastic lumber? I had not seen an LCA report on the topic, so I had to look. One Google search for "LCA wood decking" later and I had downloaded and read four LCA reports. The conclusions were the same in each report, namely that wood decking is way greener than plastic decking. Here is the conclusion from one of the studies comparing ACQ (copper preservative treated) wood to plastic:

C. A. Bolin, S. Smith, Life cycle assessment of ACQ-treated lumber with comparison to wood plastic composite decking, Journal of Cleaner Production 19, 620-629 2011

Please notice that when I discovered a material that is greener than plastic for decking, I didn't refute the findings or hide them. Instead, I presented the facts to you. That is what proper scientists do. I am not writing this book to glorify or defend plastic. The goal is to present the facts, so that people like you can make wise choices. I had no idea that wood was that much better than plastic, and this finding completely changes my view on the type of decking I would choose. I wondered whether wood is the greenest solution in other areas too. It turns out that it is. For example, natural cork comes out ahead of plastic corks and aluminium closures in LCA.

Evaluation of the environmental impacts of Cork Stoppers versus Aluminium and Plastic Closures, PwC/Ecobilan - Final report October 2008

Other renewable fillers have been proposed over the years. For example, plant-derived fillers including jute, hemp, sisal, flax, and coir are often presented as alternatives. I own a book edited by Clegg and Collyer that proclaims some of these reinforcing fillers as the next big thing. However, that book was published in 1986. All the work was already done back then, and yet commercial use never took off. Why is that? In my experience, new technologies often take 15 years to gain real traction, but if a technology is still not adopted after 30 years or more, then either it doesn't work on a technical level or is too expensive to be practical.

Mechanical Properties of Reinforced Thermoplastics, D. W. Clegg, A. A. Collyer (Eds.), Elsevier New York USA 1986

SOCIAL MEDIA AND THE PRESS

When False Claims Are Repeated, We Start To Believe They Are True – Here's How Behaving Like A Fact-Checker Can Help, Matthew Warren, Research Digest September 17th 2019

Social media is a cheap and powerful tool for repeating information. It is this new pathway that facilitates the spread of misinformation like never before. Perhaps the only way to counter the onslaught of bad information is with the extensive repetition of the truth. We may need marketing campaigns that help us find the path back to reality.

Scientists said:

I can personally vouch for their finding because that is how this book came to be written. I saw statements that I knew to be flat-out lies released by environmental groups, much like the claim that plastics last for a thousand years as we discussed earlier.

Here is another example of a scary headline. This is the kind of headline that compels interest. It attracts clicks, and clicks are what generate advertising dollars. The message is clear: according to the headline, plastics are a curse.

The Earth's climate is paying for our addiction to plastic

Every stage of the plastic lifecycle releases harmful carbon emissions into the atmosphere, contributing to global heating

The Earth's climate is paying for our addiction to plastic, The GUARDIAN, Carroll Muffett June 25th 2019

They make the point that plastics production creates CO_2, and that removing plastics would therefore mean less CO_2 and less warming. That argument is so naïve even my children can see through it. What would we replace the plastic with? We know that the replacement materials create far more waste and vastly more CO_2 as well as using more chemicals, water, and energy. The argument doesn't hold water and it's shameful to try to trick us with this faulty thinking.

Instead of being alarmed by a sensational headline, we should get some perspective:

"The daily activities of individuals create – on average – an annual carbon footprint of approximately 14 tonnes of CO_2 equivalents per capita. Of this, just 170 kilograms of CO_2, or 1.3%, is attributable to plastics. This is a tiny figure, considering that of the rest of the activities that contribute to an individual's carbon footprint, 18% is on leisure and recreation, 14% is for space heating, 13% is for food, 7% is for commuting and 6% is on aviation."

Plastics' contribution to climate protection, Plastics Europe – Association of Plastic Manufacturers

They went on to say about CO_2 emissions and plastics:

"... for every tonne of emissions created during production, 7 tonnes
will be saved over a product's lifetime."

The impact of plastics on life cycle energy consumption and greenhouse gas emissions in Europe – Summary
Report, H. Pilz, B. Brandt, R. Fehringer, denkstatt GmbH, Vienna, Austria 2010

The message is clear. Plastics create a huge net reduction in carbon dioxide. Of course, the journalist in this case was too lazy to check the facts. The truth would have ruined their story. That's actually the tedious part about writing a book like this one. It is a lot of work to go and check every fact and provide the citations so that they can be independently verified. It's certainly not enjoyable, but it is professional.

As I always say, "Get the facts before you act!"

CONCLUSIONS

The public has been brainwashed with a set of lies. We now know that they are lies because the overwhelming scientific evidence says the exact opposite. We are told plastics harm the environment when multiple lifecycle analyses show they are usually the greenest option and that replacing them would in fact be harmful. We are told that plastics cause a waste problem when in truth, plastics comprise only 13% of solid waste. Furthermore, plastics have dramatically reduced waste and replacing them requires 3-4x more material leading to far more waste, more carbon dioxide, and more energy consumption.

Lies repeated are perceived as truth, but that does not make them true. An enraged public has demanded action, and their demands have been met by companies and politicians alike. However, we now know with certainty that pandering to the misinformed public has harmed, rather than helped, the environment.

It is time to reverse course and start again by making wise choices based on solid data. We also need to crack down on organizations that spread lies unopposed, as they distract us from the task at hand.

Lie #6 – Environmental groups protect the environment.

Truth – Environmental groups advocate actions that not only distract us from the real issues but are also proven to harm the environment.

CONCLUSIONS

CONCLUSIONS, PERSPECTIVES & THE PATH FORWARD

The public has already formed strong opinions about plastics, but those opinions are based on sensationalist journalism with no scientific basis whatsoever. Plastics have been tried and convicted without evidence. When making important decisions that will affect our future and our children's future, we need to check the facts. That's what wise, caring people do. If you have read this book, then you are one of those people, and I salute you.

As Christina Hoff Sommers said:

"Be somewhat skeptical and don't get too carried away with a cause before you check the facts. If you've got good information and moral energy that's moral progress...if you've got bad information and moral fervor, that's fanaticism and history is one long lesson in the dangers of combining misinformation and moral fervor."

Christina Hoff Sommers PhD

Feminism, Free Speech, & Gamergate | Christina Hoff Sommers | WOMEN'S ISSUES | Rubin Report

Make sure you are on the right side before you start fighting, because if you don't, you will end up doing more harm than good.

Make sure to aim at the right target before you shoot

Plastics have been tried and convicted in the court of public opinion. Unfortunately, the trial was conducted without any evidence. Instead, our views are based on a barrage of rumours that are spread both online and in the mainstream media. However, this topic is too important for snap judgements because our future—and the future of our children—depends on making wise choices today. I went in search of hard data and found that the science on plastics and the environment was thorough and comprehensive, and it was a staggering task to collect and read hundreds of scientific articles in order to present it here for you. That is no doubt why this is the first book to present the whole picture in one place.

First of all, we learned that lifecycle analysis (LCA) is the best tool available for determining what is green and what is not. It allows us to estimate the total environmental impact of materials from cradle to grave. By summing up the energy consumed, the transportation impact, the pollution produced, the carbon dioxide emitted, the waste created, and so on, LCA allows us to make informed choices about the products we buy and use in our everyday lives. Looking at LCA studies around the world, we find that plastics are usually the greenest option. They are greener than paper, cotton, metal or glass in most cases. That means that switching from plastics to those materials actually harms the environment by creating massively more carbon dioxide, more waste, and more pollution. Solid wood is often greener than plastic, so for applications where wood and plastic are both viable, such as decking or wine corks, it is worth considering wood over plastic. Each type of material has its own strengths and weaknesses, and they are all applicable for certain tasks. When more than one material works for an application, we can use LCA to pick the friendliest alternative. No tool is perfect, but LCA is the best one we have, which is why it is accepted by companies, governments, and environmental NGOs alike when assessing environmental impact.

Plastics are said to be responsible for creating a waste problem, but the data prove otherwise. Firstly, plastics represent a small fraction of waste generated (11-13%). Other materials, especially paper and cardboard, create massively more waste. Another surprising finding is that plastics have dramatically reduced overall waste production. People suggest phasing out plastic, but that means using 3-4x more of the replacement material. Therefore, replacing plastics would be disastrous and ultimately lead to a deluge of waste.

The public blames plastics and manufacturers for litter. However, we know with utter certainty that it is people themselves who are to blame. In the US, over 80% of litter is dropped intentionally. For instance, every adult in the US carries an average of two credit cards and yet these small pieces of plastic are nowhere to be found on our pavements, in our rivers, or on our beaches. These pieces of plastic do not "make their way into the environment". Why? Because they have value, so we look after them effectively. It is human nature to blame anyone or anything except ourselves, but in order to solve the litter problem, we need to look in the mirror and face the true cause of litter. It is us. Knowing that human behaviour is the real cause of litter makes it much easier to address. We can educate our children and take steps to ensure that everyone acts responsibly. Taxes collected when products are sold should be used to clean up any remaining litter.

Microplastics have come under scrutiny, and the public is justifiably concerned about their safety. Clearly, such materials do not belong in the ocean—but what are the consequences, if any? Although several studies have indicated serious issues, it turns out that those studies are scientifically invalid and therefore meaningless. In contrast, the properly performed scientific studies show that microplastics are predominantly non-toxic PE and PP. Not only are they safe, but they can actually trap toxic chemicals in the ocean, thereby protecting fish and marine life. Of course, even though most microplastics are harmless, as a society we must stop pumping plastic into the oceans so that the concentration of microplastics will be dramatically reduced.

The public is enraged and demanding change. Tragically, they are demanding changes that are harming the environment because they have been badly misinformed. But how did the public become so misinformed that virtually everything they currently believe is untrue? One culprit is a certain type of environmental group that synthesizes lies in order to attract donations.

- Environmental groups have us focused on plastic waste when paper waste is more than double the amount.

- Environmental groups have us focused on plastic bags when they are the greenest option and are not even a significant cause of litter.

- Environmental groups have us focused on straws when paper straws are much worse, and straws are not a significant cause of litter.

- Environmental groups have us focused on facial wash microbeads when there is no evidence that they cause harm and are not a significant cause of pollution.

- Environmental groups have us focused on plastic pellets (which they call nurdles) when they are not a significant cause of pollution and their concentration has already dropped due to regulations.

- Environmental groups have us focused on litter in the US and the EU when 90% of ocean plastic comes from ten rivers in Africa and Asia.

- Microplastics are claimed to be toxic but they have tricked the public by presenting discredited science.

- Environmental groups tell us that plastics last a thousand years when experiments prove a plastic grocery bags disintegrate in less than one year and other common plastics also degrade rapidly outdoors.

Although many NGOs act with integrity, some of them are engaged in powerful publicity campaigns that attract attention and money but end up harming the environment through bad advice. We need to expose such bad actors and silence them.

So, where does that leave us? The public are demanding changes and the net result is harm to the environment, meaning more waste, more carbon dioxide, more pollution, and so on. Policy-makers listen to the misinformed public because they want their votes and companies listen because they want their money. If we want to make progress, then we need to change course. First, we need to have facts, and this book aims to help in that regard. Next, we need to spread those facts, and that's where I need your help. Please make sure to tell your friends and family about the findings of this book. Let's make sure that teachers are aware too, so they can teach our children the truth. Soon, I will present at our local elementary school to educate the staff and students. Major corporations have asked me to educate them and their customers. Perhaps you know a politician who should be informed. Maybe you know the CEO of Kroger and can ask him why he plans to ban plastic bags, which are the greenest option we have. If you really care, then please spread the facts so we can create a brighter future for us all.

The good news is that the plastics paradox has been solved. It turns out that plastics are a force for good. We can use them to enable our modern lifestyles and to protect the environment at the same time. No material is perfect, but we now realize that plastics are the wisest choice. They reduce waste, reduce carbon dioxide emissions, reduce oil consumption and are usually the greenest choice. That's what the science shows us.

Looking to the future, some trends are already beginning to emerge. Scientists have found ways to make today's petroleum-derived plastics from natural, renewable, plant-based feedstocks. PE, PP, nylons and polyesters have been made this way and some of those products are already gaining popularity. Braskem led the way with PE, then Neste and LyondellBasell announced commercial-scale production of bio-based PE and PP from renewable materials. P&G have created PureCycle Technologies[SM], a new process that washes used PP on a molecular level, making as pure as pristine new material. Also, companies are now signing large contracts to purchase post-consumer plastic which encourages recycling investment by ensuring a steady demand. No doubt, progress will continue in the coming decades.

More information can be found at plasticsparadox.com

The site will be used to present a lot of supplemental information including hundreds of scientific articles I could not include here as well as addressing any new science that comes to light. Speaking engagements can also be booked through that site.

SHORT BIOGRAPHY

Chris DeArmitt PhD FRSC

PRESIDENT – PHANTOM PLASTICS LLC

Chris is considered one of the top plastic materials experts and problem-solvers in the world, which is why companies like HP, Apple, Exxon, P&G, iRobot, Eaton, Total, and Disney come to him for help.

A deep understanding of materials combined with high creativity allows Chris to quickly solve even the toughest challenges. As one example, he solved a serious production issue that had plagued BASF for 30 years and cost them millions. Chris has also received six open innovation cash prizes, placing him among the top 0.01% of innovators.

In 2016, he published the book Innovation Abyss which reveals the true reasons for innovation failure and the proven path to success. In 2018, he was featured on CBS's 60 Minutes with Scott Pelley as an expert witness in a class-action lawsuit related to Marlex mesh plastic implants.

He helped thousands of women get settlements. Later television appearances include Sky News and the BBC.

Chris has a multitude of granted patents as well as numerous articles, book chapters, encyclopaedia chapters, and conference presentations to his name. He is an award-winning keynote speaker on plastic materials, environment, and innovation-related topics.

As seen on...

Dr. Chris DeArmitt
President
Phantom Plastics LLC
Cincinnati Ohio, USA
chris@phantomplastics.com
phantomplastics.com

Printed in the USA
CPSIA information can be obtained
at www.ICGtesting.com
LVHW060605230823
756032LV00010B/466

9 780997 849929